CW00765686

# Bessie Dora

Brook Cottage
Avenbury
Bromyard

Hor

My Darling Enid

I have kept my
promise to write tonight
darling and to thank you
for a lovely week-end. I
enjoyed every minute I was
with you question the
only trouble is that there
were not enough of them.

It has been a very
tiring day today I suppose
that is because I had
a late night last night.
But I suppose I shall
have to take the blame
for that, though it is
your fault really for
keeping me out so late.
I hope you did not

# Contents

# Family Tree

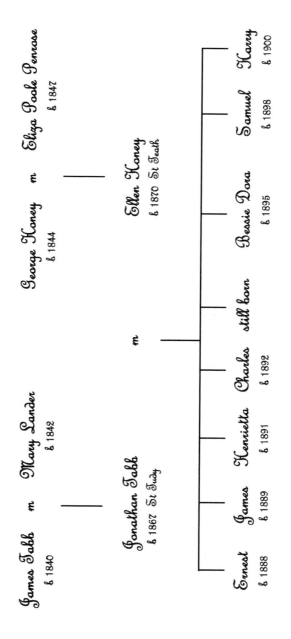

James Tabb
b 1840

m

Mary Lander
b 1842

George Honey
b 1844

m

Eliza Poole Penrose
b 1847

Jonathan Tabb
b 1867 St Tudy

Ellen Honey
b 1870 St Teath

m

Ernest
b 1888

James
b 1889

Henrietta
b 1891

Charles
b 1892

still born

Bessie Dora
b 1895

Samuel
b 1898

Harry
b 1900

# Prologue

*Winter 1931*
*Much Cowarne, Herefordshire*

She's made an attempt at a pie, but she's not a good cook. More incriminatingly, she's used the last remaining money in the jar to buy some scraps of meat from the butcher. There's been an ongoing feud with the range ever since they moved into the farm cottage, despite her attempts to clean out the ashes and polish the top. The contraption always seems to be either terrifyingly hot or only lukewarm in the bottom. She wishes she had stuck to the usual stew of swede and turnips.

She knows he'll be cross at the lack of a decent meal after toiling all day and at the waste of money. He's always gruff, even when she hasn't given cause to upset him. The children are used to the cold silences and find things to occupy themselves elsewhere. They're young but they understand and they don't take sides. They just wait for the dust to settle.

The last time there was an altercation – she couldn't remember what it was about now – both she and Arthur were seething. He lifted her off the ground, swung her up just like a sack of cider fruit and deposited her in the water trough in the yard. She was wearing her neat clothes, her little skirt and jacket that she had saved up for when she was a servant girl. Her only thought when she hit the cold water was a fear the clothes might shrink and be useless to her. She would never forgive him if they shrank. She despised the rough clothes that she wore for the farm work, and this little suit was a comfort.

Arthur clomps into the kitchen with his boots still on. He does not look at her and pays no regard to the pie on the side.

'Job's done here!' he barks. 'I've been laid off. Pack yer bags, missus, we'll be gone in the morning.'

He pushes past her to get the horse's harness off the hook. 'I'll see to the nippers,' he grumbles. 'They can stay with me sister till we get settled somewhere.'

She had tried hard to make a home of it, this little house that was theirs for as long as Arthur worked on the farm. In truth, it was better than where she was born, but somehow the rough cottage in Cornwall was not as mean as this. Her father had been a labourer, a carter, looking after the horses and driving a wagon, so it was not as if she had expected anything better in life. The years working for the family at the big house had shown her a different set of standards and a place where manners were important.

When she was about seven, her father had decided that they should up and leave Cornwall. She didn't have any say in the matter, just like now. No time to get used to the idea. Just pack your bags and leave what you can't carry. The same thing was happening again. That familiar feeling of being dispossessed, not so much of material goods but of the sense of belonging, took hold of her again. The feeling of frustration seemed to make a ringing sound in her head.

She looks at the miserable failure of a pie. Taking the solitary kitchen knife from the drawer, she cuts two portions that might satisfy her son and daughter. She would quickly put two apples in to bake. She takes the rest of the pie outside and feeds it to the neighbour's pig.

Why wait until the morning to leave? She would go now.

# PART 1

*1901*
*St. Tudy, Cornwall*

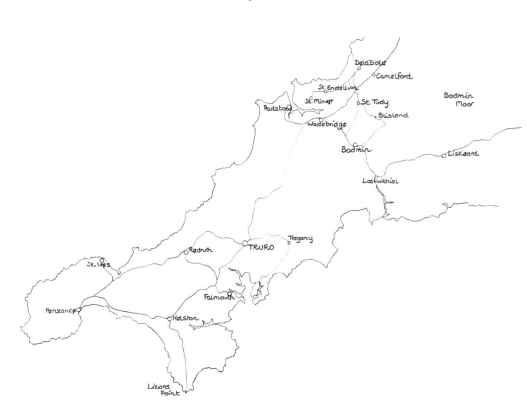

# Chapter 1

## *Looking after Samuel*

Bessie Dora is already awake and hears her father's heavy tread as he descends the stairs. His first job will be to give fresh water to the horse and just enough feed to give the mare energy for the day, but to keep her hungry, sharp, keen to pull the cart.

Bessie's younger brothers, Samuel and Harry, stir only momentarily as she slips out of the bed. They ease across into the space she has left. It's warm, hollowed, and their faces reveal the pleasure and comfort the extra space brings, even though their eyes stay closed.

Charles sleeps in a separate bed. He is the fourth child of seven, only a couple of years older than Bessie, but he thinks himself no longer a child and resents that he has to share a room with them. He watches Bessie rise and make for the door, but says nothing.

She wants to know if she can go with her father today. She'll ask as soon as he's finished with the horse. He finds her useful, she knows that, but it depends how far he's travelling, who he's got to see… and her mother needs her to look after the younger ones, run errands, fetch water and milk.

The kitchen smells of cabbages, mingling with a trace of horse sweat which lingers on the harness hanging by the back door. She'll not argue with her father if he says no.

Ellen cuts a hunk of bread as the tea brews. She wraps it in muslin with a small piece of boiled bacon. Bessie figures he's travelling a fair way if he needs to take a meal with him.

When he's halfway through the door he catches her expectant eye.

He shakes his head.

'Not today, Bessie Dora,' Jonathan says. 'Maybe tomorrow if the gaffer wants me to get the winter fodder from Blisland.'

She is trying to think what tale he had told of Blisland. She has never been, but she knows some of their folk live there. Everything he does seems to be an adventure; the places he visits so much more exciting than her little world of St. Tudy.

Jonathan wipes his greasy hands down his shapeless and coarse trousers. They are high waisted and the loose belt rests below. Ellen makes sure he has a clean white shirt but his waistcoat and jacket are heavy and stiff with dust and dirt. He wears a cap just like everybody else and is proud to be a carter. He is sharper than most, and honest. He can judge the value of things, including his own worth, a skill which he uses in trading. He enjoys the banter in bargaining and patiently procures a fair price.

Bessie has inherited many features from her father. She has thick, dark wavy hair that now reaches her shoulders. Her hazel eyes are bright, just like his, and she is quick to learn. She listens attentively but is frugal with words, using no more than she needs to explain herself. It is from her mother that she has learnt other traits, including the deep-rooted feeling of injustice. When something upsets her, she screws up her resentment and wraps it around her like a coat.

Their cottage is in Poor Row, not far from the village pump. It has two rooms down and two up. The rubble stone walls stay damp to the touch for most of the year, although the slate roof is sound. Her mother rubs away at the windows with a rag as the dust from the carts quickly blackens them. It is not in her nature to be particularly house proud, but the folk in the village gossip if certain standards are not met. 'Cleanliness is next to Godliness,' they say and people like Ellen who stray from the regular church to the chapel are scrutinised all the harder. She cleans the front step daily to keep them from carping and to avoid spiteful remarks. Jonathan smiles and tells her not to worry what other folk think. She says she doesn't, but cleans the step just the same.

There is a stone barn alongside the house where they keep the horse. A ladder reaches to the storage loft above, with a window facing over the yard at the rear. This is where the two oldest boys, Ernest and James, sleep much of the time. They are mostly unconcerned with the cold and don't mind the straw mattresses, but they slip indoors when it is freezing and lie by the range.

In a corner of the barn, an old wooden trestle sits, which Jonathan uses for holding pieces of wood for sawing. Bessie turns it into a make-believe horse when she is looking after Samuel, and it is his favourite plaything. A bit of old carpet thrown out from the vicarage lays across the frame and acts as a saddle and they use the broom to represent the horse's head and tie on bits of string for the reins. It has a tail made of real hair which Bessie has collected when grooming the mare. When they play, she picks Samuel up and he swings his legs either side of the horse. She teaches him how to lean forward and how to dig his heels in when he wants to gallop faster.

Samuel adores her. He has just turned three and she is nearly seven. While he fears the other older children, in Bessie Dora he has absolute trust. Bessie takes him for a walk every day to help him get stronger. When they go a distance out of the village, Bessie takes the small pull cart her father has made, so that Samuel can ride when he feels tired. It was intended to carry firewood, with a set of wheels salvaged from something Jonathan found. Two short planks for the bed and some more timber for the low sides means it is solid, if a mite heavy to drag uphill with the rope. Bessie has found that Samuel weighs nothing in comparison to the firewood.

Today, she takes him up to see the Hollow Oak, making a wish when they stand underneath the branches, as is the local custom. There is folklore attached to the ancient tree, and Ellen has told them that any wish made under it will eventually come true, so long as it is made with God's blessing. Bessie wants to ask Samuel what he has wished for. She studies him as he screws his eyes tight shut, and almost forces the wish up into the tree.

Bessie takes two acorns and presses them together in her hands which she holds up to pray. I wish that Samuel grows up to be big and strong and that we never be parted, she says to herself.

'Here,' she says to him, passing him an acorn. 'Keep that safe and I will keep mine safe, too.'

# Chapter 2

## *Winter*

They walk through the St. Tudy churchyard; Ellen with Bessie and Samuel walking alongside her, and little Harry nuzzling into her shoulder, under her shawl. The wind has been fiercely keen of late and there is barely a leaf left clinging to the trees. The skeletons of the oaks stand out against the clear blue sky and the winter sun picks out the frosted lichen on the gravestones.

Ellen slows her pace, as is her habit when she nears the gravestone of her grandmother, Rebecca Kellow. She is buried in a quiet corner of the graveyard, well removed from the church, and shares this resting place with others of Ellen's forebears, some with the name Honey and some with Kellow. The family tie to the area is a strong one, going back many generations.

Bessie and Samuel wander off and play with the glistening strands of the cobwebs that hang from the nearby trees. Ellen runs her fingers over the ornate carving of the angel on the top of Rebecca's gravestone. The stonemason has incised the letters of her name very deeply, and despite the age, the words can be made out clearly. It is a simple inscription, without sentiment. Ellen feels the frozen particles of moss on the sides of the stone. They crunch in her fingers. Other stones tell a fuller story, of where the person lived and their life history. Rebecca's stone simply has a name, Rebecca Kellow, and dates, 1829 to 1864. She reads out the inscription to Harry, even though the child is asleep on her shoulder. She tells him that this is his great grandmother and that she must not be forgotten.

Some from the village feel it odd that Ellen still finds solace and reverence within this space, being that she no longer attends the church. It is strange also that she has such a strong feeling towards Rebecca, as Ellen was not born when her grandmother was buried here, but there it is nonetheless, a deep attachment to the place. Ellen feels it to be the most beautiful place on earth.

It was Ellen's mother, Eliza Honey, who brought her to this spot. Eliza would sit by the grave and talk aloud; talk as if Rebecca could hear, tell her everything that was happening and seek her advice.

Just like her mother, Ellen feels calmer and has a clearer mind about what to do, after sitting in this spot for a while. It is a special place; a place where she can feel a connection to older, wiser people who have the same blood as she has and who have trodden the same stony paths. She knows they will help her if she feels troubled.

It does not matter that she now attends a different church. She still carries this place in her heart. She believes that one day it will be her resting place also, since the Methodist and Bible Christian churches have no licence for burials and no graveyards. She likes the idea of being at the edge of this graveyard, tolerated and allowed in, but not too close to the church. The thought of not being buried here would trouble her.

The graveyard is kept tended and neat. Ellen places no flowers on her grandmother's grave, content instead for nature to provide decoration according to the season. At present there is little to see, the yew and holly berries having gone and the snowdrops, daffodils and catkins yet to appear. What does it matter, Ellen thinks, the frost makes it pretty.

Ellen says a little prayer and raises her eyes to the sky. The world always seems a better place after her visit here. She's more settled in herself now and laughs at a pair of blackbirds tussling over the leaves

19

on the ground, looking for worms and grubs. She calls quietly to Bessie and Samuel to come over and see.

They leave the churchyard by the gate in the corner and Ellen gives a final little nod to Rebecca's grave. She gives Harry a kiss on his forehead and pulls the shawl up around him. She has jobs to do and she must hurry on, but she is in a lighter mood now and the children sense this and are happy.

They pass the old Clink and the Cornish Arms, where the drinkers inside sound convivial and cheery. Ellen knows that Jonathan will not be inside as drinking is not his habit.

'We have a message to deliver to Old Tom at the smithy, don't we Bessie?'

Bessie nods. She likes Tom, and often stops to watch him at work on her way to and from school. He is used to her not saying very much and it does not bother him. He is much the same. When his wife was alive, he thought she did enough talking for them both, and didn't see the need to share his business or thoughts with anyone else. What was the point in just passing the time of day? It was a distraction from his work and so he would keep his head down over the forge. That was until his wife, Rose Lobb, died some ten years ago. He woke up to find her cold in bed beside him. Day by day since then he has talked to the villagers more and more. He remembers the names of the children and their birthdays.

Ellen nudges Bessie and tells her to give Tom the message.

'Father says the mare is favouring the one foreleg and he wants you to take a look.'

'Tell him to bring her over first thing,' Tom says, looking directly at the girl. 'Tell him also that I'll need help with a wheel. It's the corn drill belonging to Jago. Reckon just your father and me can manage, it being a light wheel.' He looks up at Ellen for a sign that this will be agreeable. Jonathan and Tom have a good understanding and help each other out. There is a mutual respect which comes from hard labour and a knowledge of horses.

'I don't think you've seen a wheel being fitted on the binding stone before, have you, Samuel?' he says to the boy without looking up.

When there is no answer, Tom looks across at Samuel who is holding Bessie's hand.

'What do you think, young man? Do you want to come and help? Can be exciting with all that steam coming off. You carry on getting bigger and stronger and if you're made of the same stuff as your dad, you can come and be my mate in a few years' time.'

Tom looks at Ellen. 'I might be needing a young pair of hands to help out,' he says. 'Thought a bit back that Ernest or James might want to try smithing, but they're fixed up now, ain't they? Doing a bit of carpentry, I hear. That's a skill if you has a feel for the wood.'

She nods while trying to work out just how old Tom might be. It seems rude to ask, but she can't help feeling he might be leaving it a little late to wait for Samuel to be his apprentice.

'There's something for your pot there, Ellen, if you wants it,' Tom says. 'I was given this old rooster as payment; it's been plucked an' all. You cook it and you can bring me a dish over. I'm too busy with this and that.'

The following day feels almost like a family outing. Jonathan has got the mare ready and persuades Ellen to bring Harry along, too. Bessie has pulled the hand cart round for Samuel to climb in.

Tom watches the mare as they walk towards him. He bends down and lifts her near foreleg and examines the hoof. He mutters something to Jonathan who steps forward and strokes the mare's neck and shoulder. Tom takes the foreleg between his knees so that he can remove the old shoe. He cleans out the hoof and then takes his knife and lightly nicks inside the wall of the hoof. Bessie watches the pus dribble out and she squeezes Samuel's hand.

'You need to tend to this, regular,' Tom says. 'Then she'll be fine. Bring her back in a few days. Now, let's be fixing that wheel of Jago's.'

They watch as Tom heats the metal ring inside the forge, making it red hot. Ellen tells the children to stay outside the forge, so Jonathan picks Samuel up and puts him on his shoulders to get a better view, just as he used to do with Bessie. Tom takes the trouble to explain to Bessie and Samuel just what he is doing and why. When he is needed, Jonathan puts Samuel down and is ready to help. The two men carry the ring over to the binding stone with long wooden tongs and fit it to the wheel.

Jonathan tells Bessie to get water from the pump. She is quick and together they pour water over the rim of the wheel so that the metal band cools and shrinks and the fit is tight. Tom checks the bond and is satisfied.

'Maybe you should come and help me, Bessie,' he says, 'you're a good 'un, that's for sure.'

'What, you mean drive a cart?'

'I mean you help people. You're kind, and don't have to answer to anyone.'

'I'm not such a free spirit as you think, Bessie Dora. Mostly, I'm trying to earn us a living.'

They reach the coast. Jonathan keeps the reins slack, allowing the horse to find her own way down to the shore. He trusts her instincts and sound footing. They are after 'float oar', the well-rotted seaweed, and any other detritus that will help fertilise the land. The small inlet at the back of the cove has trapped dozens of unsuspecting fish and crabs. Bessie is not put off by the smell. She has accompanied her father before when collecting unfit barrels of pilchard that hadn't cured properly and were useless for anything but spreading on the fields. They could be obtained cheaply, save for the labour of fetching and returning the hogshead barrels.

Jonathan tells her to hold the horse steady, and keep her faced away from the sea. The waves unnerve her and she is apt to rear up and tip the wagon unless she is distracted. He knows what he needs to forage from the shore and what he can sell to the estate owners. He's made it his business to learn the terms of the leases of the tenant farmers. There are obligations specifying the type and quantity of manure that must be spread on every acre to ensure a healthy crop and maintain the richness of the soil. If he supplies a good wagonload to start with, they'll ask for more, he figures. There's a need for good salt, sand and seaweed where the crops include potatoes and other roots. It's hard work digging on account of the tides and the shifting sand. He knows of others who have been caught out trying to get their wagon too close, or not heeding the incoming sea. On the last trip he made, when he brought Bessie's older brother, Charles, along to help, there had been a difficulty. The boy had proved inattentive and let the horse wander. One of the wheels had got stuck in the sand, and Jonathan had to spend valuable time digging it out.

He inspects the back of the inlet, in a hidden away place where the dead fish build up into thick deposits. The best place is always Backaways Cove where the tides leave the float high and dry, and where he can get the horse close down to the shore.

As he works away, he can hear his daughter singing to the horse, keeping the mare calm and comforted. His daughter's got the knack, he thinks, the same gift he inherited from his own father, which was to gain the horse's trust. More than that, she is committed to the moment, simply doing what she needs to do.

When he figures they have sufficient load that the horse should be asked to carry no more, he signals to Bessie Dora to turn the horse round and to bring her closer. He starts to haul the float into the wagon checking all the time that it does not sink. He smiles at his daughter, pleased with the way she is wrapped up in helping him.

On their return journey, Bessie asks if she can hold the reins. She sits tight to her father, and he puts an arm round her in case the horse stumbles.

Jonathan tells her how well she has done.

'Did I do better than Charles?' Bessie asks.

'You did,' her father answers. 'You don't like him much, do you?' he asks. 'Why's that? Has he done or said something?'

'He's a liar,' she says vehemently. 'He told me the horse did just what he told it to and that I wouldn't be able to handle her like he did and that he shovelled as much float oar as you did and I wouldn't be able to do that as I was useless and a girl and I shouldn't be going as my place was helping mother and that if anybody should go with you it should be him.'

'I see,' says Jonathan, amused at the tirade. 'You should have told me this before. Did he say anything else?' he asks.

'He said that if anything happened to Samuel while we were away, then I should be damned forever.'

# Chapter 4

## *Lent*

The boys sling the rabbits down onto the kitchen table, knowing that their mother is out at chapel. Ellen would not have allowed her sons to bring the dead animals into the house, especially not at this time of year. She would have packed them off to the barn so that the butchering could be done there, and Ernest and James would have obeyed. They might think themselves young men now that they have started to bring some money into the home, but the older of the two is not yet fourteen, and they still fear Ellen's temper.

Now they are boisterous and in high spirits. They've caught rabbits before, but only when helping the trapper, Bill Johns, lay the snares. They show off and parade the rabbits round as trophies. It's easy to scare Samuel so they soon tire of baiting him. They turn their attention instead to Bessie and dangle the limp bodies round her shoulders.

The dead creatures are small, nowhere near adult, and there's more fur than meat. Samuel begins to cry and Bessie hugs him. She wonders whether he is crying because the rabbits are dead or whether it is the bullish uncaring attitude of the older boys that upsets him. She hates their spitefulness towards things weak and helpless. She tries to soothe him and hopes desperately that he doesn't have one of his fits.

'Bill says they're easier to skin while warm and fresh,' says James.

Ernest looks Bessie in the eye. 'How 'bout you skinnin' 'em, Bessie?' he says.

'I'm not afraid to,' she says, taking the rabbits by the ears, one in each hand. 'Just show me the one time, and then I'll learn.' She looks at Ernest, meets his eye, matches his stare. 'Best do it in the barn though, unless you want mother to give you a good hiding.'

She has deflated their arrogance. They start to make excuses for not butchering the animals straight away. It might be best if they were left to hang, they say, but they can't remember whether they must gut them first. They recall Bill saying to leave the butchering for a day or two, but only if the weather is cold, otherwise the meat turns bad.

'He told me to press the bladder to get the piss out before gutting,' James recalls, 'but I weren't watching when he did it.'

The boys decide it's best to put the rabbits in the barn and to wait and ask their father what to do. They hang them on the wooden trestle and let the bloody snares drape down. It means nothing to them, but the magic that Bessie and Samuel feel for the make believe horse has been instantly shattered. Samuel won't play in the barn while the rabbits hang there, so Bessie nods silently towards his small cart and he hops in. When he timidly asks where they are going she says she knows of a hiding place, somewhere where they won't be bothered by anyone.

She had found it by chance when she had been out delivering a message to the stockman at Polshea. She was nearly past Penvose House when the geese charged out, as they always did, raising a din. This particular day there was one bird that seemed to lie in wait for her, under the laburnum tree. No matter how fast Bessie ran, it seemed to be catching her. It frightened her more than any dog in the village, and certainly more than her brothers. The bird managed to nip her leg, and it was only by flapping her skirt that the goose backed off sufficiently for her to make an escape.

It was after that she found the den. She had stopped at Logan's Rock, at the crossroads outside the village. The big granite rock served as a landmark for travellers. Snivelling and rubbing the red weal on her leg, she thought she would hide at the back of the rock where no-one could see her, but there was a thick hedge on either side and she couldn't get through. The blanket of gorse and crab apple repelled her. It had grown at a strange angle, pushed grotesquely back by the wind, and it was too tough and tight to crawl through. Frustrated even more now, she clambered up onto the rock and could see all around her. She didn't want to be seen; she wanted to hide away from the world. Beneath her she could make out an opening, a hollowed out area where the trees and bushes leaned right over, like a shelter. She could tell it had been formed by the sheep pushing in from the field on the far side. It must have felt snug for them, the rock and bushes providing protection from the keen wind. She climbed down into the opening. The soil had been trodden down hard and it felt cosy and dry. It would be impossible for her to be seen. She lay down and curled up on the warm earth.

Bessie had thought that she would show no-one her hiding place. It was her sanctuary. She had been back there many times. It amused her that she could hear people coming and going on the road, but they were unaware of her.

When they are in sight of the rock, Bessie stops pushing the cart. She leans down and whispers to Samuel that they are nearly there.

'It's my hiding place,' she says. 'I'll let you share it, but you mustn't tell anyone else. Promise?'

Samuel promises.

'Bissy… am I bad, Bissy?' he asks.

'No, Samuel. Course not. Why do you think that?'

'I thought I must be bad to have the fits. You love me though,

Bissy. I know you do.'

'We all love you, Samuel. I get to look after you as mother has to look after little Harry. And she knows that I can look after you, so that's alright, isn't it?'

'I wish you were my mummy,' he says.

'Oh, Samuel, don't say that. She's nothing but good, our mother. Father says she gets torn up inside sometimes, not knowing who to care for most.'

When they near the rock, she tells Samuel to get down from the cart, which she then hides as best she can behind some scrub growth.

'If you want to see the den, you'll have to climb up. I can't pull the cart up here,' she tells him.

She eases her way up and pulls on his arm to help him. His curiosity spurs him on. He wants to feel cocooned somewhere. Somewhere that his brothers don't know of; somewhere safe. They can hear voices on the road from this place, hear if anyone is coming, but they can't be seen. Nobody would ever know they were there.

They stay until they begin to feel hungry and Bessie realises that she should have got him back ages ago. Her mother will be fretting. She just meant to take him out, to calm and amuse him until he was sleepy. Instead of which, he now says he wants to stay in their den and not go back.

She pushes the cart quickly, roughly, but Samuel doesn't seem to mind. She tells him that he's really driving the cart and he must sit tight as they're going very fast. He screams with excitement when they get to the pond in the village and he can see small frogs jumping around at the edge of the water. She slows the cart for him to see, and is just a little bit cross when he steps out. He kneels down and leans forward, with his nose almost touching the water. He is happy and his world has become that pond.

They arrive back at the cottage in the twilight and Bessie anxiously puts the cart into the barn. She notices the rabbits are no longer hanging from the trestle. The snares have been cleaned and put away. There's the sound of raised voices from the kitchen. She can hear her father and older brothers saying how they're going to cook them in the left over fat. Ellen is arguing that it's a sin as it's Lent and they're not to eat any meat. It's food for free, they say, and beggars can't be choosers. Jonathan is trying to calm matters. Why should they give up meat when they can get it free?

Best not take sides, Bessie decides. Best to stay out of it. She tells Samuel that they must eat whatever food they are given, and not to make a fuss.

'If it's the rabbits, don't cry, Samuel,' she says.

# Chapter 5

## *The Serpentine Stone*

Bessie Dora and Samuel are taking the path to Tremeer. The track is dry and firm during the summer months and Samuel's wheeled cart skips over the surface. It is a journey they have made many times. A mile there, and a longer mile back when she is tired and her legs and arms ache from pulling her brother along. This time they are going further, further than she has ever taken Samuel before. She hasn't told anyone of her plan, in case they tell her not to go. Bessie is sure they can make it if Samuel doesn't play up and they don't dawdle along the way. Her mother will find out, of course, and she might get scolded, but it will be worth it. She is determined to see the serpentine stone for herself. The stone that has been crafted into the most magnificent fireplace in the whole county. The stone that has a significance; a special meaning.

Bessie never tires of listening to her father tell of how he went to the shores of the Lizard and back to get the stone, on the orders of Mr. John Fortescue of Bosconnoe. The rocks on the most southerly tip of Cornwall were long known to bear a special type of marble, quite unique because of its colouring. It was said the rocks resembled a serpent, changing colour when wet and ranging from greens to bluish-purple to scarlet and olive black. Unpolished serpentine rock had been used to build several church towers in the local area, but little real value was placed on the stone until a stroke of good fortune occurred. Prince Albert was put ashore near to Carleon Cove. The folklore differed as to whether he wished to break from the royal cruise in order to stretch his legs or because he felt sea sick. Whatever the reason, the local sailor that rowed him ashore pointed out the coloured rocks and then sold him a vase that had been carved from red polished serpentine. The prince was shown other pieces made from the stone, including a fireplace. It was said that he immediately ordered a mantelpiece and pedestals for Osborne House. It became the height of fashion to follow the royal taste.

Mrs. Fortescue set her heart on a fire-surround and mantelpiece made of serpentine stone for their new house at Lanterrick Manor. The owners of the stoneworks now proudly boasted that they were supplying the richest and most well to do families in England. Despite the assurances of the company to deliver the stone intact, the Fortescues trusted no-one but their own carter to collect the piece they had chosen, and to bring it safely back.

The workshop for cutting and carving the stone was located almost on the sea shore. Jonathan told his children how he took the heavy four-wheeled wagon and two horses down to the Lizard, setting off early and with food and a blanket, not knowing how long it would take him to get there and back.

Sometimes when Jonathan retold the story, he would forget to include certain details. Bessie would always remind him.

'Ah, yes,' he would say, chuckling. 'That's right. I had to ask directions when I arrived at Poltesco and was told to head down to Carleon Cove and take the narrow lane dropping down to the sea. It was late in the day and it was very steep. I had trouble keeping the horses together. The works owner told me where to stable them for the night and that I could sleep in the barn. He said his craftsmen would attend to the final polishing of the stone in the morning.'

Jonathan always enjoyed recounting the tale. He remembered

vividly seeing the cove for the first time. It was sheltered and the shore was twinkling with different coloured rocks that were catching the light from the low sun. He studied the rock in the cliff and the pebbles on the beach. Every one was different, a different shape, size and hue. He picked up a stone from close to the shore. He fancied it as a trinket for Ellen. In the early days, he would always try and take her something back if his carting took him away from her for a night. Somehow, this touch of tenderness had become forgotten. He remembered thinking that Ellen would be pleased if he took her a little something. It might help things between them.

He told his family how he waited in the morning while the craftsmen at the works fussed over the final polishing and buffing of the mantelpiece. Not being able to help with this, he wandered along the shore. He passed the fine house built mainly of crafted serpentine, tucked into the sheltered side of the lagoon. He was told the house had been built for the manager of the works, Henry Cox.

Jonathan told how he wandered up the pretty little valley and crossed over a wooden bridge. There he picked the sweetest apples he had ever tasted. He bought an apple pasty from a lady at a cottage and had it for his breakfast. When he went back to the works, the men had still not finished. They were making a special wooden case to carry the piece and told him they would not load it until the afternoon. He was shown how to catch some scads and congers with a fishing line and was pleased he had something else to take back.

He asked one of the boys at the works if he would work on the pebble he had picked up from the beach and give it a polish, maybe see if he could fashion it into some sort of trinket. The boy turned it over in his hand and said it was a true piece of serpentine, having a real snake-like appearance. He worked on it for a while and when it had been finished on one of the machines and polished, it glowed a kind of dappled green colour and almost had the appearance of a little bird.

Jonathan recalled how it took four men to load the fireplace into the wagon. He watched carefully as they bedded it down in straw. Even so, he knew he would have to take it really steady on the way back. He trusted the horses to be sure footed and that nothing would frighten them, but the roads were pitted and poor. Even the turnpike roads were scoured of their stone and with ruts as deep as his deepest spade. If a wheel got down in one, he had thought to himself, then the wagon was bound to pitch and the fireplace would be damaged. It didn't matter how long the journey took, he had told himself, as long as he got it back safe and sound. Every now and again he would pat the pebble in his waistcoat pocket; he had so wanted Ellen to like it.

Jonathan always finished the story by saying, 'I was as pleased to get that pebble home as I was to get the piece up to the big house. And I think yer mother was as pleased as they was.'

Ellen always smiles at this.

Bessie Dora retells the story to Samuel as they make their way along the path. They cross over the rickety bridge at Tresarrett, and drop sticks into the fast flowing stream. Samuel asks if they can go and look for tadpoles in the pond nearby, but Bessie tells him that they have all grown up and that the frogs won't come out while there are people about.

'The story of the stone doesn't end there,' she tells Samuel, 'because this is a magic stone. It has been made into magic because father brought it from a magical place.'

Her older brothers, Ernest and James, talk endlessly about the stone also, now that they have seen it for themselves and touched it. They are working at Lanterrick Manor and have been there helping out for the past few months, ever since the house was badly damaged by a fire. In truth, only the north wing of the house had been affected. The master bedroom had burnt to a cinder and debris had wrecked the parlour below. There was a gaping hole in the roof, the fire having created a new opening rather than obligingly using the massive chimney stack to the side. The stone fireplace stood in the parlour, directly below the bedroom where the fire had started. It was the first thing the workmen had been asked to look for after the fire had been extinguished. Whether the fireplace had survived or whether the stone had been crushed by debris? How the fireplace remained undamaged was a miracle, they said, given all the fallen timbers and slates; but there it was. They said it looked rather more like a sooted and blackened Cornish range than a fine piece of stone, but when they cleaned it up, there was not a scratch or a crack anywhere.

Ernest and James are working hard at the house and are determined to prove themselves to be as dependable as their father. Jonathan and Ellen are delighted when the foreman, John Button, puts in a word for them and the owners agree they should be taken on officially as apprentice carpenters.

At home in the evenings, the boys give their father a full account of how the repairs are taking shape and what the gaffer has set them to do. Jonathan listens keenly to what his sons have to say about the repairs and what is being salvaged or thrown away. The roof had been made secure and watertight and the floor to the bedroom relaid. All of the rubble had been removed from around the fireplace and the stone had been repolished.

Bessie Dora hadn't thought through what she and Samuel would do when they got to the manor house. She knew that the owners, Mr. and Mrs. Fortescue, had moved out straight after the fire, being too upset to stay. They had gone to stay with relations at Pencarrow, she believed. Her brothers had said there were just one or two servants living in the house, but they never saw them. She had listened carefully whenever they spoke of their walk to Lanterrick and which path and turn they took. She had played it over in her mind. They didn't need to walk down the main drive, the boys said, which twisted this way and that. They had walked that way on the first day, and were amazed by the fine stand of chestnut trees on either side. Very grand, they said, but it added an extra half mile to the journey. After that they learned instead to turn off the road by the cattle and turnip house and then to take the path to the top of the hill.

Bessie follows the route which her brothers would have taken at first light. She pulls Samuel along in his little hand cart, reassuring him that they do not have to go much further. It suddenly occurs to her that the people working on the house may not take kindly to her being there and that she may not be allowed to go inside.

To Bessie Dora, who was used only to the cottages in the village, Lanterrick looked immense. It was a giant, she thought, standing at the very top of the hill, looking down onto the valley and Fox Hole Wood. The building looked haughty and proud and there was not a trace of any fire damage to the outside.

As they draw near, she can hear hammering and sawing, but she cannot see her older brothers or anyone else for that matter.

'What have we here, now?'

Bessie is startled. She had not heard John Button, the foreman, approach from the far side of the house.

'Please sir, we'd like to see the serpentine stone, that which my father brought here by wagon. Everybody talks about it so much. We wanted to see it for us selves.'

'Well, little lady, I think that might be possible, but I think you better leave that wheeled contraption here.'

He picks up Samuel as if he was as light as a bird, and sits him on his shoulders, telling him to hold on tightly and not let go. He takes Bessie Dora by the hand.

'Here it is,' says John, as they enter the parlour. 'It's one of the treasures of the house. The craftsmanship in the making of that is something wonderful. It was her Ladyship's wish to have the best, and it's certainly that. Better even than marble. They have 'em in the posh houses in London, yer know. You ask yer teacher. We can't quite believe how it survived. How it endured those flames.'

It was a striking piece. Bessie had been told it was all colours; reds and greys and greens. The patterns and swirls fascinated her. It seemed to be like the streaks in the sky sometimes, when the sun was waking up. It was beautiful. She loved it.

'My father said it took four men to load it into the wagon and that he was the only one trusted to drive it back here.'

John nods.

'My mother has a little piece of serpentine stone,' Bessie tells John. 'Nobody else knows this but she says it will be mine, when I'm older. Not Henrietta's or the boys'. It will be mine as a reward for looking after Samuel. I think that will be a magic stone, don't you?'

'Yes, it will. And you should treasure that and always keep it safe. Maybe pass it on to your own children some day.'

# Chapter 6

## *Pengelley and Delamere*

Jonathan has borrowed a pony and trap from Old Farmer Greenwood. That way, they would get there much quicker. Jonathan hates taking a loan of anything for nothing, but Greenwood insisted.

'Won't want a be fretting later if you don't get there as quick as yer could,' the old man had said.

There had been another accident at the slate quarry. A bad one this time. For years there had been cracks in the rock face at Bonnears Hill, on the western side. Nobody took much notice of it, but a heavy frost brought down a ton of rock. George, Ellen's father, was not working on the face that day. He was in the splitting shed in the bottom of the open quarry, but he heard the rumble. He joined other quarrymen heading towards the cloud of dust. A further fall of rock engulfed them. It took with it the weighbridge and the magazine store, and the rubble blocked the track down to the bottom.

It was the following day that news got through to Ellen. No official word had been sent, but as always, bad news travelled quickly, even to outlying villages. They said that George Honey was one of the men injured at the slate quarry, and that it had taken over four hours to get him out. There was no other news except that he had been taken home to Pengelley, and that his wife, Eliza, had been tending to him. Two other men had also been badly injured. Jonathan said straight away that they should go and that they should take Bessie Dora and Samuel and Harry with them. They would send word to the other boys that they would be gone for a day or two.

Bessie Dora had only met her grandfather on a handful of occasions, but she liked him as he seemed gentle despite the rough job he did. He would pick her up and playfully squeeze her. His big bushy moustache that stretched down to his chin would tickle her face. His whiskers were grey, but when he took off his dusty cap, his hair was black and curly underneath. She remembered thinking that he had a kindly face but that he looked tired. The last time they visited must have been a special occasion as her mother had prepared some treats to take with them. Ellen had said she didn't know why she bothered trying to bake cakes, as they never turned out as well as Eliza's. They had gone on the cart that day and it seemed to take an age to get there. Pengelley seemed quite foreign to Bessie Dora as the buildings were all made of slate, making it appear dreary, even when the sun shone. But there was a bustle to the place, with people going to shops and inns and places of worship. There appeared to be more life than in St. Tudy, more people, more children playing in the streets.

The pony and trap that carried them today was fast, faster than anything Bessie Dora had ridden on before. It was exciting to see the hedges skim past and the road almost leap up to meet them. They reached the milestone out of St. Tudy seemingly before they had even started. Samuel pointed and giggled as their secret hiding place at Logan's Rock flashed by, gone in a moment. They passed over the river at Knightsmill and drove past the church in St. Teath. Now they were seeing slate hedges and fewer trees. Soon there were no longer cattle in the fields, just poor scrub.

Jonathan is trying to talk to Ellen, to divert her from the bad thoughts that are troubling her.

'We'll get there soon enough,' he says. It's a good stretch of road now. I should know, I helped my father build it. Roadman Tabb they called him.'

Ellen says nothing. Jonathan concentrates on the road ahead and tries to calculate how much longer it will take them to get there. She cuddles Harry closer to her, wrapping her shawl round the both of them.

Bessie knows enough to stay quiet and to play with Samuel in the back of the trap. She knows it is not an occasion to be enjoying herself but even so, the day seems exciting. How different the journey is to the plodding horse and cart she has ridden on before.

The wind picks up and blows in from the sea. It deepens the frown on Ellen's face. Bessie can tell that Samuel is tiring and he whispers to her that his knees ache from the cold. She changes places with him so that the whip of the wind hits her first, and he is sheltered.

They reach the cottage where George and Eliza Honey brought up nine children. The two older sisters who had not married, Rebecca and Rose, stand at the door. There they feel more able to give enquirers the news of their father. Stoically, they mutter words and the neighbours and people of the town bow their heads and shuffle on.

From the moment they arrive it is as if Bessie and Samuel are forgotten. They are told by their father to stay outside with the pony and trap, but it is a miserable spot alongside the village pump and there is no shelter. A neighbour sees them and takes them in. They are given a hunk of bread and some soup which tastes salty, although Bessie tells the kindly woman that it is good.

After a while Jonathan comes to find them to say that their grandfather is dead. He was very brave, Jonathan said, and had been trying to save another, but that man had died too.

The neighbour agrees that Bessie and Samuel can stay with her for the night. Her own children had grown up and left, she says, and she and her husband would be pleased to hear young voices in their cottage again.

It is the first time that Bessie and Samuel have spent the night away from their own home. They are given a bed each, but Bessie quickly snuggles in alongside her brother. Samuel sleeps a deep sleep. He is warm and well fed and he likes the stone warming bottle that the woman has rested against his knees. Bessie watches over him, and it is a long time before she closes her eyes.

In the morning, when her father comes to check on them, Bessie overhears him talking to the woman downstairs.

'She's a good woman, my wife, and I'd not change her for anyone, but she's taking it hard. Her and Eliza, ther' all the time with the Minister, praying. Praying for George's soul. They're all as bad as each other, these preachers. I'm afeared for Ellen. She's fragile. We lost a child some years back, yer know, then we nearly lost Samuel. Now losing her father, too. I told her we got our other children to look after. 'Stead of that, she's saying we got to help the woman who lost her husband, him that George was trying to save. They got four young uns, and the Minister keeps saying they're in need.'

The woman says something to her father which Bessie Dora cannot hear, but she catches his reply.

'I'm not saying I don't believe in God, but we lost a child for no good reason. Now she's lost her father. What's that going to do to her? I lost my father years back, before my children were born. So now they won't know a grandfather at all.'

Jonathan calls Bessie and Samuel to him.

'Yer mother's not well right now,' he tells Bessie. 'You need to comfort yer brother. Don't let him out of yer sight.'

Bessie is pleased that her father trusts her, but later she hears the woman talking to her husband.

'It's not right. They're asking too much of that child. What if something happens to the young boy? Will they blame the girl then?

It's not her duty. They're putting on her too much. Poor mite. If something should happen, she'll run away, that's what she'll do.'

# Chapter 7

## *Leaving St. Tudy*

A month after George's funeral, Bessie begins to feel her mother is calmer and better in herself, but as she pulls Samuel's little cart back into the yard she senses that something else is wrong. She hears her father's voice coming from the cottage and is surprised he is not still out working. She hears snatches of conversation that don't make any sense, and her mother seemingly agitated. She steals a look through the open back door. Her parents stand on opposite sides of the kitchen table, and there is a tension between them.

'Young Mr. Greenwood wants us there straight away,' her father says, 'else he'll hire someone else, someone local.'

'But cannot you go, and we follow on after?' Ellen reasons.

'No Ellen, no. We have to go together and we have to make this work. It's a fresh start.'

'But Ernest and James, they'd be daft to give up working for John Button. You said so. You said he was a good man to work for. They're not children any more. They might feel they're old enough to make up their own minds.' Ellen tries to think of more logical reasons for them to stay, when all she really wants to do is to cry out that she can't leave her home.

'What will it do to Charles,' she asks, 'if we just up and move? He's been more settled of late and he's doing better at school. They said so. He's never taken to anything before, but he's trying now and he likes running errands and sweeping up in the shop. Seems wrong to uproot him.'

'I reckon we's better off with Master Greenwood. He wouldn't be going if it wasn't good prospects. I'll talk to the boys. Explain things. It's a good opportunity, Ellen.' As an afterthought he says, 'I'll leave you to talk to Henrietta. Decide what to say to her. I know she seems to like it up there at the house and I know she's been learning a lot, but she's been learning too much about fancy things, if you ask me. There'll be something for her where we're going. You tell her.'

Her father brushes past Bessie Dora on his way out, but does not seem to notice her. Bessie carries Samuel inside, still expecting her mother to scold her and ask her why the errand took so long, but Ellen has her mind on other things.

'There's a lot to do, child,' Ellen says with a deep sigh. 'We are leaving here, going away. Your father has decided. I need to go and call on the Minister to get Samuel and Harry baptised. I don't know what we're going to find where we're going, there may not be any other Bible Christians, so they'll have to be baptised now.'

'I want to stay here,' Bessie mutters.

'You can't, Bessie Dora. Look, there are good things that can come from this. We just have to accept that our future is elsewhere.'

Bessie takes Samuel into the stable to play on the wooden horse. It is not right that her father can just decide something like that, she thinks. Why was there no discussion on the matter? Why was it that neither she nor her mother had any say, any opinion that counted? Why wasn't she to be baptised along with Samuel and Harry? Was she not important enough? Bessie contemplates running away, taking Samuel with her and going somewhere, she's not sure where. Maybe to the lady in Pengelley, who gave them the soup that was salty.

Bessie kicks at the wooden trestle. She idly picks up the long handled fork which is longer than she is tall and starts to rake out the sodden straw. She will clean out the barn and wait there for her father to come back. He will be pleased with her for working hard and making things tidy. She will tell him that she and Samuel want to stay, and he will listen.

# PART 2

## 2015
## *Herefordshire*

# Chapter 1

*Douglas's Request*

Rosie looks at her mother and tries to think of the right thing to say. The tea sits stewing in the pot, the old fashioned tea cosy, which her mother insists on, keeping it warm. Rosie likes her tea weak, and is counting the minutes, the seconds, itching to lift the pot and pour out the brown liquid. How long before her mother won't fret at the pot being lifted?

The shop-bought cake sits untouched. Enid is put out, not at the extravagance or the waste, but that her daughter would not think her capable of baking a simple Victoria sponge. It is two weeks since Douglas's funeral. She has taken the sympathy cards down. Kept the ones she likes, got rid of the rest. The phone still rings with people asking how she is doing; did she want any shopping getting in; can they walk the dog? Enid thinks she would be doing fine if only they would leave her alone for a while with her thoughts.

Monty. Doug's dog. Well, only in the respect that Doug took him for most of his walks. The faithful terrier would sit forever in the garden watching the pair of them work, waiting for the odd stone or twig to be thrown.

'What's with the shoe box, Mum?' Rosie asks just to break the silence and nodding to the battered cardboard box on the kitchen table. The label on the box still professes a pair of gentleman's black leather lace up shoes, size 8, are inside.

'I keep the old photographs in there. To be quite honest, I've got a job to remember who some of these people are. I should have written the names down long ago. I know you've bought me lots of albums to put them in, but I never seem to get round to it. In a way, though, I like them all being jumbled up. I like the randomness of it, never knowing what will pop up next. In an album, there's a regimentation, they're always in the same place. This one before that. There's no surprises. Anyway, I've realised that if I don't sort them out now, everything will be a muddle after I'm gone.'

Rosie can warm to the sentiments. She likes the 'shuffle' button on her CD player, a lucky dip of what will appear next. She picks a handful of photographs out of the box, grateful for a distraction and a talking point.

'Look at that one,' says Enid, leaning across. 'I couldn't believe how many pictures Monty has snuck his way into. He's a tiny puppy in that one, all floppy ears and clumsy paws. Makes it easier to date when it was taken. Now, if I could only date some of these older photographs that easily.'

'Monty, I'd forgotten how cute you were as a puppy,' Rosie says, stroking his ear.

The fox terrier tilts his head towards Rosie, knowing that he is being talked about, but then his attention is caught by something beyond the open kitchen door. He appears to hear something rustling in the nearby shrubbery. Rosie looks out. The garden no longer looks immaculate. The flower borders are overgrown, and there are patches of clover and creeping buttercup invading the lawn. The dog goes into military action, marching across the patio and then dropping down into the hydrangea bushes. He often has to frighten off rabbits, and occasionally a muntjac deer that strays in from the neighbouring farmland. This time it seems to be a false alarm. The dog, satisfied that there is no threat, trots back into the kitchen and stretches out across Enid's feet.

'Probably just a blackbird turning over leaves, looking for food,' says Enid. 'He's very protective of me now, you know. Probably worried that I'm going to up and disappear, just like Doug. Must be very difficult for an animal to understand.'

Rosie is wondering how her mother is going to cope with the garden. Was it too soon to suggest moving to somewhere smaller? There would have to be a garden of sorts for Monty, but surely something more manageable.

As if reading her daughter's mind, Enid says, 'I'm going to have to get somebody in to help. Should have done something ages ago, but your father wouldn't have it. Said we could manage and that nobody else would prune the roses properly.'

'It's a job to find anybody that wants to take on gardening these days,' Rosie responds. 'You can always get a contract firm in to mow the lawns and other big jobs, but nobody wants to weed flowerbeds any more.'

'Your father would turn in his grave if I got a contract firm in. They use such big, noisy machinery. Do you remember the last time we took him to hospital for treatment, and we were in a queue to get into the car park? He couldn't bear to watch that young man with a great big hedge trimmer pruning the little shrubs. He wanted to get out and tell him that he should be using hand shears.'

'Yes, and he nearly had a fit when they started that leaf blower up, just to blow a few twigs away. Wound down the window and gave the guy a good talking to. Course he couldn't hear a word that dad was saying with those massive ear defenders on.'

They return to the kitchen table and look through a few more of the photographs. Rosie tentatively suggests buying a few new picture frames so that she can put some on display. She tells her mother that they have some nice ones in the gift shop across from the hairdressers.

Enid seems distracted and doesn't respond.

After a pause, Rosie enquires softly, 'Are you alright, Mum? Is there anything you want me to do?'

'Rosie, there's a photograph here you've never seen before. Your father kept it at the back of his tallboy. It's the only picture he has from his childhood. I came across it years ago, but I never said anything. I didn't let on that I'd seen it.' She passes the photograph across to her daughter.

'He's a skinny little kid, isn't he,' says Enid lovingly, 'although he looks healthy enough. I didn't know who the girl in the photograph was until he told me. That was his sister, Sarah. She's a few years older, as you can see.'

There is a pause while Rosie studies the photograph and Enid watches her.

'A few months ago,' Enid continues,' when your father knew that he was really ill, he took the photograph out to show me. He told me he had kept it hidden behind his ties and best handkerchiefs. I didn't say anything. The photograph was taken just before his mother walked out. So he was just seven, or nearly eight years old. A little while later, Sarah went to join his mother, Bessie Dora, and she became a nurse, but they didn't stay in touch. His father, Arthur, refused to discuss anything about Bessie Dora. Douglas remembers Arthur petitioning for a divorce some years later, not knowing where Bessie Dora was. So he had to register the petition with the courts and the divorce was granted on the grounds of desertion. Arthur came to our wedding, but Bessie wasn't there. As far as I know she never made contact with Arthur or Douglas again.'

'Did Dad never want to talk about her? Surely when you were going to get married, you must have talked about her?' Rosie asks.

'Her desertion was a subject we never touched on, but he did tell me a few things about her. He said she was always very kind to him. He remembered her being very calm and gently spoken. Even when there was a row with Arthur, she didn't raise her voice. And she smelt really nice, he said, not of perfume but of soap and lavender. She kept a lavender pouch on her pillow and always seemed to smell of it. She taught him how to eat nicely, which knife and fork to use should he ever go up to the big house or the vicarage for tea. He said that she had lovely manners, and her hair was always neat and tidy.'

Rosie studies the photograph of her father with his curly hair all tousled, and with a hesitant and innocent smile. His clothes are ill fitting, clearly passed on, and a rough belt with an 'S' buckle is holding up a pair of long baggy shorts.

'When we were planning to get married, I asked if we should try to find her. Douglas said no. It wasn't that he had any bitterness towards her, he didn't. It was just that he had got used to her not being there. And of course, this was all after the war. He was just so happy to be alive and to be getting married and setting up a home.'

'You and Dad always told me that Bessie Dora left the family to go back to nursing somewhere?'

'To be honest I don't know whether that was true or made up. Your dad didn't want to say anything bad about her, that she just walked out on her family. I think he had to pretty much bring himself up. Arthur was busy working.'

'I didn't realise she wasn't at your wedding.'

Enid goes across to the dresser and pulls out a large, framed wedding photograph from the drawer.

'There's Arthur. He looks really awkward, doesn't he?'

'Oh, Mum. Everybody else is so smartly dressed and he just looks as if he's slept in his clothes. Dad looks so handsome and you look gorgeous and you both look so happy.'

'I don't think Arthur owned a suit. Of course, it didn't matter to your father and me, we were just so happy. At least in the photograph he doesn't have a cigarette dangling out of the corner of his mouth, which is how I always remember him. He didn't say a lot, but when he did it was always gruff. We took you to visit him a few times when you were little. Do you remember him?'

'I sort of remember a bit. I do remember feeling a little bit uncomfortable with him. He hadn't had a shave and he smelt of tobacco.'

'He didn't have what you might call social skills, but your father said that he wasn't unkind. Douglas seemed to have a respect for how hard his father had worked, especially after Bessie left. You've got to realise that in a small rural village, a mother going off like that and leaving young children, it would have been talked about for ages. Your father must have been hurt very much to have been rejected like that. I think he was a very lonely child. Arthur moved around locally from one tied cottage to another, getting any sort of farm work he could. Your dad just accepted things as they were. That was his lot. He couldn't change anything, but it seemed to make him more determined. After we got married, and you came along, he did everything to make your childhood as wonderful as he could make it, and to give us a lovely home.'

'It just seems really odd talking about this now. Why did we never talk about it earlier?' Rosie asks.

'I was always curious about Bessie Dora. I remember discussing it with my parents before Doug and I got married. Douglas and his father lived in a village about ten miles away from where we were. My parents knew a little about Arthur from other people, but had never met him personally. It was said he was a hard worker but very rough and ready. Didn't have any manners and a real temper. My parents thought his son would turn out like him. Then when I carried on seeing Doug and I told them I was really keen, they said not to rush into anything. I think they hoped it would fizzle out. But then they got to know Doug, and they could see how polite and well-mannered he was. So we got married with their blessing.'

'What did people say about Bessie Dora?' Rosie asks. 'Did they remember anything?'

'It was said she just seemed to turn up out of nowhere. Nobody really knew where Arthur had met her. My mother was told she was a small lady, and always well dressed, although it was obvious they were handmade clothes. But then when she upped and left, nobody knew where she went to. It caused a scandal in the village. After that, people tended to avoid Arthur, although they didn't really know what had gone on. Your father just carried on going to the school in his village and studied hard. He was bright, but it can't have been any life for him at home. Then the war came along and he saw an opportunity to escape and serve his country. Thank goodness, he survived.'

'Okay. But I just don't get the point of all this now. Why should we care about Bessie Dora? She hasn't been any part of our lives, ever!'

'Rosie, I do understand that this is all a little strange. But your father, after showing me the photograph, he asked that we try and find out about her. About where she came from and what happened to her. He said she had a lilting voice. She didn't speak like anybody else from the village. And she didn't seem to know anybody or have any friends. I don't know why, but your father seemed to think we might find out something good about her. I think he was desperate to know that she didn't have a sad or a wasted life. He didn't hate her. In fact he prayed that it got better for her...' Enid pauses. 'Will you help me?' she asks her daughter. 'I'm not sure I know where to start.'

# Chapter 2

## *Sounds like Trouble*

Rosie drives back to her own house thinking all the time about her father and Bessie Dora. How come a lid had been put on this box for so long? She couldn't bear to think of her father having an unhappy childhood, yet it hadn't seemed to scar him in any way. There was no bitterness in him, as her mother had said.

She couldn't fathom the fascination that her mother seemed to have for Bessie Dora. Okay, there was a bit of mystery surrounding her, like where she had come from and where she disappeared to, but what was the point of raking over the past now? Rosie thought about the request her father had made when he knew he was very ill, namely to find out something more about her. That was surely just the parting wish of a dying man, to hopefully find evidence that his mother wasn't such a bad person after all. Even if they managed to find out anything about her, nothing was going to change the past, Rosie figured. It wasn't going to help her father.

Her small terraced house was in darkness when she arrived and she knew it would feel a little chilly and gloomy inside. Rosie remained sitting in the car wishing that she had a friend nearby that she could pop round to see for a coffee or a glass of wine. She needed company to help with the grieving process. How many times had she told people at work, give yourself time to grieve. Don't bottle things up. Talk to friends about everything, anything. Open up. It will help you move on.

All very well dishing out advice like that, she thinks. Why

don't I listen to myself? The rules at work allowed her time off as compassionate leave. She administered those rules and she knew what her entitlement was and so could have made life a little easier for herself. Instead, and without a thought, Rosie took only a half day annual leave to make arrangements and a day for the funeral itself. She told no-one what had happened. She opened up to nobody. Even Julie, her assistant, whom she could have confided in without fear of gossip, was brushed away when commenting that Rosie looked a little tired.

All she wanted now was to help her mother. They had always been close. More like good friends than mother and daughter. Perhaps there was no harm in trying to find out what happened to Bessie Dora. At worst it would be a waste of time; at best they might find out some interesting facts. Rosie knew her mother's character. She was a stubborn individual and would no doubt pursue this course of action anyway, so Rosie might as well just help things along.

As Rosie gets out of the car and searches in her handbag for the door key, a niggling, aggravating thought lodges in her mind. This is her grandmother they are talking about. What if some of her character, her traits, have been passed on? She's almost certainly inherited some of Bessie Dora's genes. What if they are the bad ones?

As she unlocks her front door, she weighs up the other possibility. Maybe Bessie was a nice lady, after all. Maybe there was a deep rooted reason as to why she left Arthur. Maybe she did pass on some good qualities, like gentleness and kindliness. Her father certainly seemed to have gained some qualities that seemed more likely to have come from Bessie rather than Arthur. But what if the bad genes had skipped a generation? What if they had missed her father and been passed onto her? What if she'd inherited the bad characteristics, those flaws that meant you were rubbish at relationships, that you couldn't commit to anyone and they couldn't commit to you?

I'm not liking this, Rosie thinks to herself. She drops her keys on the hall table, while taking a long look at herself in the hall mirror. We don't know the first thing about Bessie Dora. What she looked like. What she did. Why she ran off.

Best leave this alone, Rosie thinks. I've no time for a dead grandmother that walked out on my dad. The thoughts still keep needling as she tugs off her boots, and jabs her feet into the waiting slippers.

'No thanks, Bessie Dora. You sound like trouble. I don't think I need to bother myself about you,' she says out loud.

# Chapter 3

## *Enid talks to Doug*

'Come on Monty. We're taking a walk,' Enid tells the terrier. 'I need to have a little chat with Doug before I do anything else.'

They walk down the lane. This is the first time Enid has been back to the churchyard since the funeral. The flowers and wreaths have been removed but the earth still looks fresh and clean. Not a weed has dared to grow as yet. There is a small wooden cross. A gravestone has been ordered and the inscription chosen, but this won't be erected for several months until the soil has settled.

Enid pauses by the bench just inside the gate. She can see the grave clearly, but she needs a moment to compose herself and to decide what to do with the dog. She is fearful that if she takes Monty to the graveside, he might start digging. She looks at the dog directly and tells him to stay put and guard the bench.

Walking calmly across the graveyard, she smiles and sits down on the grass by the wooden cross in order to have a more intimate conversation. The thought occurs to her that at her age she may find it hard to get up again and maybe sitting on the ground isn't such a good idea. She directs her gaze at the little wooden cross, but then closes her eyes and speaks just loud enough for her husband to hear, as if he were still sitting in his armchair.

*'Hello Doug. I'm having a clear out of things and I want to know why you left the shed in such a state. You were always out there tidying it up. So goodness knows what you were doing all the time. I went out there trying to find a screwdriver and it was like looking for a proverbial needle.*

*Anyway, I'm not really telling you off, because I've hoarded a few things over the years as well. I've kept a lot of the letters you sent me when we were courting. You used to write to me every day to tell me how much you were missing me. I don't mind telling you, I cried when I read those letters again. You must have been so tired working all day long on that farm and getting soaked through if it rained. You never complained though, or felt sorry for yourself. You always took the trouble to write me a lovely letter. You said you couldn't wait till we had a home of our own. That was what kept you going, you said.'*

Enid looks across to the bench to check that Monty is behaving himself. She takes a deep breath and looks back at the fresh earth on the grave.

*'I've had a chat with Rosie about trying to find out more about your mother, Bessie Dora. She's going to help. I can't believe Bessie Dora was all bad, otherwise how come you turned out so well? I'm so curious about it all, and when we find things out it will give us something to talk about when I come to visit you. I've already discovered something. It was on your birth certificate. I had to look that out when I went to register your death. Your mother's maiden name was Tabb. Bessie Dora Tabb. That's definitely not a name from round here. So I guess that's where we start.'*

She surprises herself by getting up off the ground without too much of a struggle, and walks back to the bench.

'That's a lovely peaceful spot he's got there, Monty. We had a nice chat and I had the last word for a change. He misses us both, just like we miss him.'

# Chapter 4

## *The Interview*

Rosie puts on the jacket of her Wallis suit in readiness to leave for work. She is trying not to let Bessie Dora get under her skin, but she has slept badly and is feeling tired. There are dark shadows under her eyes. Months of worrying about her father replaced by concern for her mother now that she is on her own. On top of that she has to solve a mystery about a grandmother she never knew. If you're a worrier, then there's always something to worry about.

Whatever the stresses, she never lets any trace of her personal life intrude at work. Put on the face, adopt the persona, don't let it show. That is her mantra.

The interview shouldn't take very long providing the employee cooperates, she thinks. She has already checked that her hair is tied up with no strands escaping, and that her make up is as it should be.

As Deputy Director of Human Resources, Rosie is very conscious of time and protocol. She looks at her notes. Tenants in one of the Housing Association flats have reported an incident of theft. The description they gave of the man was that he was tall and lean, but fit, and that he wore a beanie hat. That only narrowed it down to about fifty of their employees. A search of the job sheets and the trades employed points the finger at one of their longest serving employees, a quiet guy who had no record of any misdemeanours.

When the employee arrives, Rosie kicks off the interview in a friendly fashion.

'Okay, William, let's hear your side of the story.'

'It's Will. I don't answer to William.'

Rosie is never one to pre-judge. Assemble the facts, hear people out and consider the matter from all sides is what she's always done. Now she must put her own emotions and anxieties aside and give the guy a chance.

Will sits there, looking unapologetic. He's in his decorating overalls and they look like an homage to Jackson Pollock. There is a long silence, but years of experience tell her to give him some time. While she waits for him to speak, she thinks back to the exhibition she went to at Tate Modern the previous year. 'Abstract expressionism.' If she told him about that, would he think she was mad? Her mind flashes back to the amazing images she saw at the gallery. She thinks of the raw energy the artist had somehow injected onto the canvas.

The staff think her distant and cold; she knows that but she figures it's how you have to be in order to do the job. Stay aloof, never fraternise or allow personal friendships to get in the way. Never take sides, form allegiances. Just in case you have to discipline someone or settle an argument. That way you can always prove that you are unbiased and totally objective. Never let there be any cause for an accusation that you took someone's side for personal reasons.

Will seems distracted, studying the picture on the office wall behind Rosie's head. It is a montage of photographs Rosie had taken while on holiday in Cornwall two years ago. They are a series of miniature images, taken from a cliff top, looking down to the sea. All twelve images, three across and four down, look to be the same picture at first glance, but on closer inspection they show the tide at different stages of ebb and flow and with the surf on the shore. Each one is unique and each is a little masterpiece of the moment. The photographs are stitched together and it is only on close inspection that you can see what the images actually are. Rosie finds the picture comforting.

'I like that,' says Will. 'It's different. Did you do that?'

'I took the photographs, but then I had them mounted professionally.'

'You can really lose yourself in that picture, can't you?' he says gently.

His words catch her a little off guard. She feels like telling him that is exactly what she does. Loses herself, when things get too much. When there is endless bickering and sniping in the office. When her boss introduces another crazy scheme that means her sitting up half the night compiling the necessary information. She would come into the office and immerse herself in the picture. She would imagine herself on that cliff top, or walking along the shore, splashing in the surf and letting the sand ooze up between her toes.

'Where's that taken, then?' asks Will.

'A remote part of Cornwall. Look, Will, I think we need to discuss why you are here.'

'Bound to be a complaint 'bout something. Whatever it is, I didn't do it. Unless it's about driving the company van out of the county. That was just a mistake. The satnav was playing up.'

'No, it's not about that and I'll forget you told me that. It's about taking a door from a skip at Belmont Road. The neighbour saw you take it out of the skip and put it in the back of your van. I mean the company van. But they say you looked shifty and they didn't think you were taking it for work purposes.'

'Nosy bastards. I thought I noticed some curtains twitching. Anyway, I always look shifty, it's because my eyes are too close together.' He tries to engage her with a smile.

'So you did take a door out of the skip. I need to explain that this is not a disciplinary hearing; it's just an initial investigation. I need to make you aware of the allegation, which I have now done. You can assist by telling me what actually happened.'

'Look, I just do the job. I put in the hours and I never skive off like the others.'

'Yes, I know, Will. I know you're a hard worker and I've never known you have any sick leave or say anything inappropriate. But, you've got to know that it is a sackable offence, stealing. So please don't take the matter lightly.'

'It was rubbish; it was in the skip. That can't be stealing, can it?' he asks tetchily.

'Technically, yes it can. The skip was on private property, so while it was still on the drive, the contents belonged to Edendale Housing Association, and as soon as the skip was removed from the premises, it was the property of the skip hire people. At no point was it your property. Just because it was discarded by someone else, didn't make it yours.'

'But the chippies had ripped out all the timber as substandard. It was shit. I'd spent a week glossing all the new doors and windows and the stair bannisters. What's wrong with removing some old timber out of a skip? I thought we were meant to be recycling stuff. It would only have gone to the power plant for burning. Where's the sense in that?'

'It didn't belong to you,' Rosie pointed out.

'Didn't seem to me that it belonged to anybody, it was in limbo.'

'What did you want the door for, anyway? Were you going to try and sell it?'

'No.'

'What then?'

'I'm making a rabbit hutch for my mate's daughter. Just as a favour, not for cash. That door wasn't rotten, but the bottom was all smashed in where the tenant had kicked it when he was off his head. Thought I could cannibalise bits of it to make the roof of the hutch.'

'It wasn't for yourself, then?'

'Does that make any difference?' Will asks.

Rosie looks at him. It didn't make any difference, but it sort of made it more excusable. It made a difference in Rosie's eyes anyway, just at that moment. She wishes she could be on the beach in Cornwall, watching the tide coming in.

Rosie believes him about the rabbit hutch. She thought that it showed an innocence. It wasn't the first time she had tried to explain a bewildering set of rules to employees. She wonders how Will would react if there was an official disciplinary hearing. Good painters and decorators were hard to come by. She liked Will and thought that he was basically honest. It was just an unfortunate misunderstanding, but it would not look good on his CV. With such an accusation he would probably have to be suspended, pending the investigation. That would mess up the scheduled redecorating works at Blackdown Road and give her another headache to sort out.

'You're wondering what to do with me, aren't you?' asks Will. 'What if I put the door back? I've not sawn it up yet.'

'I don't think that will work, somehow,' Rosie answers.

'Look, do what you gotta do. I know it's not personal with you. You're straight. Bit uptight, but straight.'

He takes out a packet of cigarette papers and some Amber Leaf tobacco and starts to roll a cigarette.

'You can't smoke in here.'

'I know that. I'm not going to light it. I don't smoke any more, gave up years ago. I just like to roll the thing and then when I feel like it,

I just unroll it and put it back. Helps me unwind.'

Rosie had noticed the T-shirt underneath the overalls. That he was wearing a ZZ Top T-shirt made her smile inwardly. Rosie had been a fan of the blues-rockers for years. The band had been around for decades, probably as long as Glastonbury. Now they had hit the headlines by being booked to appear there. What would Will think if he knew she liked their music, or that she had made the trip to Glastonbury several times? But that was years ago, before the festival became synonymous with glamping and celebrities. She brought her mind back to the present.

'I haven't misunderstood you, have I?' she asked. Were you rescuing the door so that it wouldn't get damaged any further? You said it was a good door apart from the bottom panel. That can be replaced, can't it?'

Will was beginning to catch on. He didn't say anything but rubbed the end of his stubbly chin.

'Where will I find the door in the morning, if I want to go and inspect it?' asked Rosie.

'It'll be in the paint workshop.'

'Right, I suggest I meet you there at seven-thirty and you can show me the door. I can then file a report and that should be the end of the matter. Just a misunderstanding. And thank you for coming in and explaining.'

'No problem. Thanks.'

Will squirms around in his chair, looks across at Rosie and tries to adopt what he thinks is a look of gratitude.

'By the way, if you fancy coming down to the Majors Arms Friday night, there's a bit of a shindig going on, I can buy you a drink.'

'No, I don't think that would be appropriate.'

'Well, not a drink then. Just come along. It's good. I'm allowed a guest as I play a bit. So you wouldn't have to pay on the door. Just mention my name.'

'Thanks anyway.' She opens the door and watches as he walks down the corridor.

One of these days, thinks Rosie, I might do that, I just might. She is surprised at herself. There's something in his rough and oddball character that she likes.

# Chapter 5

## *Enid's Cottage*

When Rosie visits the following week, her mother is still sorting through old photographs. She hands Rosie a small black and white print, no bigger than a post-it note.

Rosie recognises her mother and realises that the baby in the photograph must be her, although there are no features really to speak of. Just a slightly grumpy expression. There are two other ladies in the photograph, one very elderly and with pure white hair. She has a lovely, serene smile.

'I love this photograph,' Enid says quietly. 'It was taken just after you were born and it shows four generations. That's really special when you think about it. You, me, my mother and her mother, too. Douglas thought you were the most precious thing on this earth. He was almost too frightened to hold you to start with.'

Rosie squeezes her mother's hand affectionately. They both feel immensely proud.

'I've been sorting out all the family papers that we have. All the birth and marriage certificates. Some of them are really difficult to read, so I went and got your father's big magnifying glass. That's been quite a help. There is so much information on them, you'd be surprised. And it's not so many generations ago that some of our relations couldn't read or write. They just signed their names with a cross. Think of that.'

Rosie was thinking how good it was to see her mother so full of questions, curiosity and enthusiasm. Perhaps it was best to be supportive. At least it was keeping her mum occupied. She wasn't moping around after Dad.

They go for a walk round the garden and Rosie notices that there are weeds cheekily emerging from the gravel paths. The side border, on the other hand, looks neat and tidy. As if to signal that someone has been busy working, a fork stands proudly dug into the reddish clay soil. The Michaelmas daisies are a riot of colour, and the white Japanese anemones sway in the breeze like little paper hankies.

'Have you been busy working, Mum, or has somebody been in?'

'No, it's all my own work. Seemed disrespectful to your father, somehow, not to at least have a go.'

'It's looking lovely. Dad liked this time of year especially didn't he?'

'He liked all the seasons, although as he got older he was less keen on winter. I remember last spring he got very excited at the first show of snowdrops… shouted to me in the kitchen. I wondered what on earth was going on. He was waving his walking stick around, pointing at this and that.'

Rosie waits as her mother seems lost in her thoughts for a few minutes. She looks around, admiring the autumn colours.

'I couldn't be bothered tying up some of the dahlias. So I just cut off the ones the slugs had got to. And I didn't realise how quickly bindweed could spread. Your dad would be cross though, for not putting the fork away, and I forgot to lock the shed.'

Rosie can't think of her father being cross at that, but she doesn't say anything.

'Monty sat there all day, looking at me,' Enid continues. 'I'd turn round and find him watching me with an expression that seemed to say, *you're not doing that right*. Oh and I had a robin come and sit on the rim of the weed bucket. It all felt very calming. I even forgot to get lunch so I treated myself to fish and chips last night.'

'My goodness, did you drive all the way into Hereford for those?'

'No, the neighbours, Linda and Brian, were going in to get some and asked me if I wanted some. So, I popped them in the oven when they got back, had a bath and ate them in my pyjamas. What do you think about that?'

'Sounds wonderful.'

'Yes, they brought back a sausage for Monty. Very naughty. I did get vexed with them, though.'

'What, about the sausage?' asks Rosie.

'No, they said I should take a holiday, go on a cruise! What a ridiculous idea.'

'I'm sure they were only trying to be helpful.'

'I don't want to go on a cruise. People would just think I was out to get another husband when I've only just lost the love of my life. It would be awful,' Enid says.

'No, I can't picture you on a cruise, but maybe a short break somewhere?'

'I don't want to go anywhere. I don't want to leave the dog. Monty is confused enough as it is without your father around. Poor dog has become very protective of me. Keeps chasing things out of the garden.'

'Mum, do just what you want to do, but if you do want to go away, we can find someone to look after Monty. I'd have him but he'd be on his own all day while I'm at work, and meetings often drag on.'

Enid tells her daughter as gently as she can that she's finding some peace and comfort in the garden and in talking to Douglas at the graveside, and she doesn't need to run away on a cruise.

Rosie stops for petrol on the way home and browses the magazine rack as she queues to pay. Her eye catches the title *What's in My Past*.

She takes it, and not having time to open it before she gets to the till, just pays for it thinking that it will probably be a waste of time.

When she gets home she feels unsettled, vulnerable. She knows she should get on with the housework, put a load of washing on, but instead she starts to flick through the magazine. Smiling faces of people that have traced their roots way back and found descendants that were transported to Tasmania. Others that are seeking to prove that they are somehow related to royalty.

What if she opens up a can of worms looking into her genealogy, she wonders. Maybe there are some things it is better not knowing? She starts to tell herself that whatever they find out about Bessie Dora, it won't make her, or her father for that matter, different people. They are who they are. Rosie often wonders about people at work, when they act strangely and go off the rails. Is it something in their background, their genes, or is it simply their environment, the circumstances of the time? She looks at the magazine again but is bored by the articles on DNA sampling and genetics. She decides to give the magazine to her mother, maybe she will get more out of it.

On a whim, she decides to go out again. She has just remembered Will's invitation to the gig at the pub. She needs a distraction and she is curious to hear him play.

# Chapter 6

## *The Majors Arms*

Rosie enters the pub by the side door. She is unsure about staying for the whole gig, but curiosity has got the better of her, and she wants to see just what sort of band Will plays in. She can see him setting up the amplifier and trying to sort out the leads and cables for the electric guitars. He has his back to her and does not see her as she sneaks by. The place is packed but Rosie can see a free seat and small table in the corner. It looks a little forlorn, the one empty seat. All the other chairs have been taken and rearranged to accommodate groups and couples sitting elsewhere.

Rosie slumps down and realises the empty space around her and the single chair broadcast to the world that she is on her own, while the rest of the pub buzzes with people. They are a diverse bunch. Young farm workers from the local area, lads from the nearby town, a rowdy table of women making a racket in the snug, and a group of bikers in the side bar who sound as if they are from the west country.

She wishes she had got herself a drink as soon as she came in. Now there is a queue at the bar, and she doesn't want to look conspicuous or lose her seat. Her confidence is beginning to ebb away and she thinks she might just slide off before the music starts.

Will is experiencing the usual chaos of trying to set up the equipment in a confined space. Trying to regain her composure, Rosie wonders if she should go over and speak to him, but thinks better of it. She wants to stay unnoticed, just an observer. There's no importance to her being here, anyway. It's just curiosity on her part.

He was trying to be gallant in the only way he could think of. The invitation to come was just a bit of a thank you. Nothing more than that.

As soon as Will spots her, he makes his way across.

'I didn't think you'd come,' he says. 'It's great that you did. Only trouble is, our main singer can't make it, so looks like I'll be doing most of the vocals, which isn't great from the audience point of view. What can I get you to drink?'

'Just a tonic water please.'

'Okay. I'm going to get myself a pint. Or two. We'll be on in a few minutes and I'm getting a bit nervous. Here, can you take care of my jacket and phone? There's nowhere to put stuff over there.'

'But I might not be staying to the end.'

'Course you will. Be rude not to, and you've got to tell me how I do. Look, I'm getting a bit twitchy so I'm going outside to roll a ciggie. I'm not going to light it, I just need to do something.'

'But if you're not going to actually light it, why do you need to go outside? Or are you thinking that you might light it?'

'No. But I get really fed up of people saying, 'You can't smoke that in here'. I better go and check what the guys feel like playing tonight.'

Rosie is quietly excited to see Will up front and chatting to everyone. She thought he would be lurking at the back. She is nervous for him, but he seems laid back enough as he introduces the band and jokes with the audience.

'Right then. Listen up. We are going to play some old style rock numbers,' he says, 'followed by some new bits, a few light bits and then some numbers that don't seem to fit in anywhere else but we like them. We're starting with *Come Together* by the Beatles. It's a good test of whether we can get it together tonight. Later, I'll give you ample warning of when I'm about to do my solo, which is my version of *Tangled up in Blue*. That's the best time to piss off and get some more drinks in.'

After that, he didn't say much, just got stuck into the music. There was a good atmosphere in the pub and Rosie didn't feel conspicuous any more. She was caught up in the music and was enjoying watching and listening to Will do something that he clearly loved. He had a deeper voice than she expected, not quite Leonard Cohen, but it resonated.

It took Rosie back in time, listening to live music, and she realised just how much she missed it. She had great memories of going to clubs and concerts, often in murky and faded backstreet clubs.

When he comes over she leans across and thanks him. 'It's been good to get out,' she says 'Actually, Will, I've really enjoyed it. Never figured I'd be coming back to this place, but it's been fun. I haven't actually been out anywhere since my dad died.'

She wasn't looking for sympathy. The words just came out of her mouth as a statement of fact.

'Oh, okay. I didn't know. Sorry. I noticed you were off work the one day, but I didn't know the reason.'

'You noticed I wasn't at work. How come?'

'Job sheets never got sent down. We was told that your boss, in your absence, decided to try out a new procedure and everything got screwed up. We spent all day trying to work out where we was supposed to be. That man is such a pillock. You would never allow stuff like that to happen. God knows what trouble that prat would get us into if you weren't there to sort him out.'

'I don't think we'd better talk about work. Let's talk about your band instead. Why are you called Major B?'

'It's just a bit of fun. It's short for Major Balls Up, and we thought it was kinda witty being as we play at the Majors. We were told we couldn't use that name so we just shortened it. Live music. You can't beat it. It's Andy's band really. He does most of the organising. We just go along with what he says, although I get a say in what we play. We got a couple of songs that we wrote. If it's going well, we throw those in sometimes, but I wasn't going to risk it tonight without Andy.'

'It's an eclectic mix of songs,' she says, laughing. 'That was a strange one to end with, *You got a Friend In Me.* I didn't know Randy Newman wrote that one.'

'You obviously never seen the film *Toy Story.*'

'No. Can't say I have,' she answers.

'We found that if we ended with too strong a number, you know a sort of hell for leather sound, then people would get all pumped up, and occasionally, you know, there were a few fights. So we started playing a slower, sweeter number, and everyone calms down, buys a nightcap which pleases the landlord and goes home in a good frame of mind. Also, it's nice for the couples who want a more romantic kind of evening.'

'My mum and dad would have come here when they were courting,' Rosie tells him. 'That was ages ago. I think that's partly why I wanted to come tonight. Mum won't believe it when I tell her.'

'It probably hasn't changed that much,' he says draining his glass of beer. 'They don't go in much for improvements.' He looks up to study a hop bine hanging from the main oak beam which was from last year's harvest. It was the same colour as the tobacco stained walls.

'Is your mum taking it okay?' he asks gently.

'I think she's doing really well, but she's delving into the past. She wants to find out about my dad's mother. What she was like. What happened to her.'

'You should encourage her. If she's interested, go with it. Might be a treasure trove of stuff.'

'I just wonder whether any good can come of it,' Rosie says. 'All I know is that she was called Bessie Dora.'

'I didn't know my mum and dad when I was a kid. I was adopted. Came as a bit of a shock when they got round to telling me. That was when my real mum died, and they thought I should know. Said they meant to tell me before. So then they gave me my real dad's name and told me what he did for a living. Took some courage, but I found out stuff about him, and then later I met him. He wasn't bad, just couldn't cope with some things. Had a breakdown. I spent ages researching all the family history. Really got into the ancestry stuff. You should try it. I can help you if you want.'

'Maybe Bessie Dora had her reasons, too. She left my dad when he was little. I just can't see how we would ever get to the truth.'

'You'll never know till you try,' says Will. 'Come on, it's last orders. Let me get you another drink.'

Rosie rings Will as soon as she gets home from the pub. 'Thanks for tonight. It was great,' she says.

'Glad you enjoyed it.'

She hesitates just for a moment.

'Can I take you up on your offer?' she asks him quietly. 'To try and find Bessie Dora. You've convinced me it's a good idea.'

'Sure. How about tomorrow? It's my Saturday off. We could meet in the library,' he suggests. 'They've got loads of family history records; we're bound to find something.'

# Chapter 7

## *Visit to the Library*

As soon as they are inside the spanking new library building, Rosie feels uncomfortable. She wonders to start with whether it is Will. She hardly knows him and now she's about to trust him with her past. She's not sure she wants to open up in that way, to lay herself bare. It's almost as if she feels pressured, trapped.

The library had seemed a good idea when Will suggested it last night. Now it seemed so impersonal. She felt on edge. She might be about to reveal a secret from her family history without any privacy or forewarning.

Will can tell she is edgy and has retreated into her shell.

'You're not comfortable with this, are you?' he asks gently. 'Is it because I'm here?'

'No, it's not you. It's me being silly. It just doesn't feel right. I don't think I want to do this here. Sorry to have dragged you out.'

'We don't have to do it here,' Will says quietly. 'We can go to a coffee bar where they've got wifi and do it there.'

'I think I'd like to go home,' Rosie answers.

'Okay, sure, no problem.'

'No, I mean... I would like you to help me with this, but not now. I'm sorry to have dragged you out.'

'You said that already,' he says, laughing softly. 'Look, don't worry about it. It got me into town. I was meant to come in but kept putting it off.' He shifts his weight to the other foot and hooks his thumbs into the pockets of his jeans.

'There's a favour I need to ask you. My daughter's getting married and I need to buy a suit. I wouldn't have a clue what to get. It's just not my sort of thing and I don't want to show her up. You've got style. You're always really smart, make the best of yourself. Come with me and help me sort it out? We could grab a bite to eat afterwards.'

The request is met with silence.

'I could try and argue it's your responsibility to make sure employees don't make complete tits of themselves on important occasions,' he says, 'or I could say that I don't have anyone else I can ask which would make me sound like a complete saddo.'

Rosie smiles at the suggestion that because she is in charge of Personnel she somehow has a moral duty to help him. The line about it being her responsibility to see that he didn't look like an idiot on the day was nonsense, but even so, the way he had worded the request touched her. She hated the thought of him looking awkward. Weddings could be such stressful occasions. At the back of her mind was the wedding photograph her mum had shown her where everybody was dressed smartly, except for Arthur, her dad's father. He must have been wearing his best clothes but they were scruffy and rumpled. Everyone else was smiling and enjoying the day. Arthur just looked as if he didn't belong.

'Yes, I'll help. Wouldn't want you turning up in your jeans and pro men's work boots.'

'Great,' he says. 'I'm going to look ridiculous in a suit. They just don't make one my size.'

Rosie had been aware of his long legs and bounding stride as they walked into the library. She had difficulty keeping up with him. She'd also noticed that he had a strong upper body, probably from the manual work. She couldn't quite picture him going to a gym.

'Depends how much you want to spend, really,' she says, bringing her mind back to the problem in hand. 'If you don't mind spending a bit, then a good tailor can take care of that. It just means you can't buy anything off the peg.'

'I don't mind splashing out to get properly rigged up; just can't stand all the fuss and bother.'

'Is she worth it, your daughter?'

'Yes, of course she is,' he answers.

'Do it for her, then, but you should talk to her first to find out what she's got in mind. You need to know what the groom and best man will be wearing. So many weddings are themed these days, which can make things easier or more difficult.'

'All she said was not to wear jeans or a T-shirt.'

Rosie takes a sideways glance and ponders what he would look like in a suit. She can't help wondering whether the daughter takes after him.

'When is the wedding?' she asks casually.

'A week on Saturday.'

'You are kidding!'

'No. A week on Saturday, somewhere in the Cotswolds. I forget exactly where.'

'I suggest we go to Symonds now and hope they are not busy. They do in-house alterations, although you're not exactly giving them much time.'

Rosie gives a little shake of her head. Men; why do they always leave everything till the last minute?

In the gents outfitters they are greeted by Damien. Rosie leaves them to it, and sits down on the leather sofa. She feels that she has done her job for the moment, actually getting Will to the shop, and lets Damien take over. She settles back to look at the quick crossword in her paper. She has finished all the clues bar one when Will comes over from the changing rooms wearing a crisp white shirt and a dark grey flannel suit. The jacket fits beautifully across the shoulders but the trousers are slightly too long even for his long legs. The thought strikes Rosie that she didn't realise till now what a neat little bum he'd got. He has his hands in his pockets and a shy grin on his face. He is clearly hitting it off with Damien and trying to treat the whole thing as a joke, but underneath she can see he's way out of his comfort zone.

'Apparently I'm an odd specimen, the likes of which they haven't seen before, but they're treating me as a challenge.'

'What do you think?' trills Damien. 'They've got to be taken in of course, at the waist, and shortened a smidge. Shall you be wanting a waistcoat or just jacket and trousers?'

The assistant kneels at his feet and folds up the trousers, quickly inserting the pins that are kept in his sleeve.

'No idea,' says Will. 'I'm leaving it to you two. I'm just supplying the body.'

'Yes, well it might help if you try to keep still and stop hopping around,' Rosie chips in.

They decide against the waistcoat as it makes Will feel as if he is in a straitjacket.

A female assistant wanders over and asks Rosie what outfit she will be wearing to the wedding, so that they will co-ordinate. Rosie is just about to explain that she isn't going to the wedding when she hears Will let out a low groan, and looks up to see him thump his forehead with the butt of his hand.

'I'm such an idiot. Yes, of course, you should come with me. Please. It will be better if you are there. The speech and everything. Selma, my ex, she'll have her new bloke with her. It'll be far better if I'm not on my own.'

'No is the simple answer. I'm not muscling in on your daughter's wedding. It would be deceiving people, letting them think we were a couple. Just think in years to come, when you all look back at the wedding photographs, everyone would be asking, *who's that with Will? Who did he bring along just for the occasion?* No, thank you.'

'It doesn't have to be like that. It's not such a bad idea.'

Will is told to come back in two days' time for a fitting. He looks across at Rosie as if to ask if she will come back too. She smiles and her eyes tell him no, you can do that one on your own. They walk out, both feeling just a touch light headed.

It doesn't take long for Will to relax, the anxieties he had shown while trying on the suits have been put back on the rail. She admires the fact that he seems comfortable in his own skin.

'Thanks for that,' he says.

'It's okay. Quite happy to help.'

'Does that mean you're coming to the wedding?'

'Absolutely no way,' she replies emphatically.

# Chapter 8

## *The Vine*

'Type in Bessie Dora Tabb and press on search,' says Will. 'It's best to make some notes of what you find and where you find it, in case you need to go back to it again later. I used to drive myself nuts finding out something about my old man and his family. Then another question would enter my head, or I'd want to check on something and I couldn't remember where I'd found it in the first place.'

They are sitting side by side at the computer in Rosie's house and are looking at a website for family history. Will suggests that they start with the latest published census record which is for 1911.

Will watches her as Rosie studies the screen. He remembers when he started trying to trace people through the census and other records. It all seemed very confusing at first. It was like a jigsaw puzzle sometimes, trying to work out where various people fitted in.

'You have to work at this,' Will explains patiently. 'It's not like those programmes on the TV, tracing their ancestors. They've got loads of researchers doing the work for them. It's not that easy.'

He is familiar with the records and how they are displayed, but she just feels like a new kid at school, thrown in at the deep end. She wasn't expecting the census returns to be handwritten, and has trouble reading some of the entries. Also, she is not really sure what she is looking for.

'The information will have been transcribed,' Will explains, 'so there is a typewritten copy, but believe me, there are often mistakes. The people copying out the names and dates may not have been able to read the original writing either, and may have just guessed at it. So if you don't check the original, you might miss something vital.'

The search for Bessie Dora's name has brought up the household of a Mr. John Frederick Zimmerman, living at The Vine at Tarrington. Rosie knows the house. It's in the village next to where her mother lives. He is listed as a silversmith and widower. She looks at Will and shrugs her shoulders. She can't see the relevance of this.

'Keep scrolling down the names,' he says, his eyes intently on the computer screen.

'There she is!' shouts Rosie. 'Bessie Dora Tabb, twenty-one, single, general domestic servant. Wow.'

'You see, you need to look at all the information. So John Zimmerman is head of the household. He's got several servants so must have been quite well off. Living in the same house there's Ulric, his son, twenty-one and single. Then there's a Jessie Tandy, forty-nine, housekeeper, another servant, name of Elizabeth Caldwell and then Bessie Dora at the bottom of the pecking order, I'm afraid. Are you disappointed that your grandmother was a servant? You weren't expecting her to be gentry, were you?'

'Don't know what I was expecting. The Vine... I used to walk past it when I was a kid. Great big house with a lovely brick wall and gates. I used to wonder what it would be like to live there.'

'There's something you haven't picked up on yet. At the end of this column, it tells you where Bessie Dora was born.'

'St. Tudy, Cornwall. That can't be right.'

'I bet it is. No reason to lie about where you came from.'

'But all our family are from Herefordshire. I need to try and get my head round this. Dad never said anything about his mother coming from Cornwall.'

'Perhaps he didn't know,' Will suggests.

'Can we look up the next census, the one for 1921?' Rosie asks.

'Fraid not. They're still under lock and key. It's to do with privacy laws. They don't publish records for about a hundred years. Records tell where people were on census night, and they were not always where they should have been, if you catch my drift. So we'll have to wait a little while for that information, but there are other records, electoral registers and the like, and we can go further back in time with the census.'

'But how does that help?' she asks. 'I want to go forward. I want to know what happened to Bessie Dora after this.'

'It helps to go back in time, as well. You have to try and work out their life history. Where they came from. Who their parents were. How many brothers and sisters they had. What they did for a living. It's all relevant and by getting to know all of that you can build up a picture of someone.'

'Do you really think I've got Cornish blood in my veins?'

'It's not exactly a crime, you know,' Will says, laughing. 'They serve a Cornish ale down the pub. Tribute, it's called. Fancy trying it?'

'Sorry. I'm really tired tonight and I've got to prepare for a meeting tomorrow.'

'No worries,' he shrugs. 'Think I'll go and scribble a speech for the wedding. Don't suppose you'd care to give me a clue on that?'

'Don't try to be too clever or cute, and don't say anything you know will embarrass her.'

'You've still got time to come, you know, keep me under control,' he says with a grin.

She gives him a kiss on the cheek and opens the door for him to leave, surprised at how soft his skin feels.

The following day, Rosie pays a surprise visit to her mother. She suggests they go for a walk as she has something to tell her. They stroll down the old Kings Highway in Tarrington, past the former school which is now the village hall. There is a stillness. The new main road bypasses this stretch of village and the lack of traffic and noise gives a calming, trouble-free quality. Monty is let off the lead as there doesn't seem to be any mischief he can get into.

Rosie has a strange feeling when she sees The Vine, knowing that her grandmother lived there. It is an imposing three storey building, set further back than the smaller cottages alongside, behind a high stone wall. The house is built of mellow red brick and unrendered stone, much of it hidden from view behind wisteria. When they are near, they pause and look in through the half open medieval wooden door in the wall, a relic from much earlier times.

'You know, Mum, I always wanted to live in that house. I thought it looked quite mysterious. What would you say if I told you that Bessie Dora was a servant girl there?'

'Well, I'm blowed. Now that's something to tell your father!'

'That's not all. It looks like she was born in Cornwall. Will's looked up the census records. He says there can't be two Bessie Dora Tabbs, it's such an unusual name for round here.'

'Who is Will?' interjects her mother.

'Just someone at work who has experience in these things. He's got me signed up to a family history website.'

They spend a while staring up at the house. There is a clean symmetry to the frontage, an imposing porched front door with tall windows on either side, and two further rows of windows above them. The red tiled roof harbours two very small windows, suggesting some cramped internal space within the eaves.

'I was always intrigued with this house, too,' says Enid. 'I wonder which room was Bessie's?' she muses. 'Presumably one of those small windows in the attic on the top floor.'

Even though they have seen it many times before, they are now viewing the house with new eyes. They try to conjure up the past and picture how life might have been. It was such a quiet, tucked away little place.

'I'm just wondering how Bessie would have met Arthur? It's well off the beaten track, isn't it?' Enid comments.

'Will says you've got to try and envisage how life would have been back then,' says Rosie.

As they stand gazing up at the house, a black labrador bounds out through the opening in the wall and dances around Monty. A tall, well-dressed man, whom they take to be the owner, tries to catch the dog and fusses around them. He introduces himself as Richard Price and politely asks if they live nearby as he has not seen them before. Rosie is more than a little surprised and embarrassed when her mother begins to tell him of their search for Bessie Dora, and how they know she worked at The Vine.

'Extraordinary,' Richard says, seeming to enunciate every vowel.

Rosie thinks he is just being courteous and expects him to quickly lose interest, but he seems fascinated by what her mother is telling him.

'You may have heard of the Zimmermans, then,' he says. 'Interesting family. Very wealthy. This was just their country house, of course. Lived much of the time in Birmingham where their manufacturing business was. Produced high class silverware and jewellery. Even had their own hallmark. Your ancestor, was she the housekeeper? I gather John Zimmerman became rather attached to her. Left her quite a legacy in his will.'

'No, she was just a general domestic servant, according to the census records,' Rosie replies.

'I don't suppose you've got anything here belonging to those times?' asks Enid hopefully. 'It's so long ago.'

'As a matter of fact, I have,' says Richard. 'Quite fascinating, really. John Zimmerman was a widower when he lived here, just like me. His son, Ulric, had died earlier in the war, and had not married. So when John died, most of the estate was left to charities. Gave a lot to the cathedral school. The house here was auctioned off and a couple bought it, but they shut off all the top rooms, the servants' quarters. Boarded them up to keep down the running costs. I suppose they didn't need them for anything. It was only when I came here that those rooms were opened up again. I'd be delighted to show you, if you wanted to come in and take a peek.'

Rosie starts to make an excuse, saying that they don't want to put him to any trouble and they'd got the dog, but her mother has other ideas. Enid bustles forward grabbing Monty's collar and at the same time telling Richard how lucky they are to meet him.

'Of course, a servant wouldn't have entered by this front gate, would she?' Enid enquires. 'Bessie would have been taken round the back, presumably.'

'Yes, she'd have gone in past the outbuildings and stables. I can show you round there in a minute, if you like. That's the reason I bought the place, really. Plenty of room for my cars. I'm a bit of a collector. The house is far too big for me, but I needed lots of garaging.' He leads the way inside and shuts his own dog in the kitchen.

'I found some account books and some diaries from when Zimmerman was here,' Richard tells them, 'in one of the upstairs rooms. I could go through them, see if there is any mention of your relative. Do you know exactly when she was here?'

'We know from the census she was here in 1911. We're not too sure either side of that,' Rosie pipes up. 'She married my grandfather,

Arthur. We don't know how they met.'

'Fascinating. Let's have a look at the top floor. Do you want to go up by the servants' stairs? Retread her footsteps, so to speak?'

As they climb the twisting stairs, they seem to be slipping back into the past. The rooms in the attic are small and seem to be unused. There are still odd pieces of furniture about, a chair and a dresser in one of the rooms, but no beds. The floors are boarded and there are no carpets or mats, but even so, the rooms feel friendly and secure.

'I think Bessie would have felt quite safe up here,' Enid muses. 'Such a lovely view across the fields to the hills.'

'Very quiet and peaceful, but I'm wondering what on earth was there for Bessie to do when she wasn't working?' questions Rosie.

'I shouldn't imagine she was given much time off,' Enid says jokingly.

'There might have been the odd dance to go to,' Richard suggests, 'and there was the pub, depending on what sort of girl she was. Of course the house was used for wounded soldiers during the First World War. Quite a few public spirited people let their houses be taken over as military hospitals. This one was unusual in that the Zimmermans stayed on here as well. Perhaps they had more cause than most to take a stance. It must have been pretty crowded and from what I've read, the servants had to do their bit to look after the injured. Perhaps your grandfather was here, if he'd been injured.'

'Arthur was in the war, I remember Doug telling me,' replies Enid, 'and he got injured in his foot. Maybe he came here and Bessie looked after him?'

Enid sits down on the solitary chair, not because she is tired, but to get a feel for the space about her, to take in where Bessie would have sat when she wasn't working downstairs.

'The records I was telling you about are over there. Bit dusty, I'm afraid,' says Richard apologetically. 'I honestly didn't know what to do with them when I came here. Seemed wrong to throw them out as they're part of the history of the place.'

Rosie walks across to the dresser which stands against the far wall. The shelves are stacked with red leather-bound ledgers, some with faded gold lettering on the binders, and an assortment of other journals, cash books and inventories.

'I can have a good look through or you can borrow some of them, if you like,' Richard offers, 'and there are a few photographs of the house being used as a convalescent home during the war. Here, look,' he says, passing a framed photograph across to them, 'the wounded have been taken outside on their beds. Fancy that, and they're all waving at the camera.'

Enid is itching to look inside some of the books and ledgers, but the sheer number of them is daunting, and they have left Monty tied to the boot scrape by the front door. Richard says that he will see what references he can find to Bessie Dora in the ledgers and books and then invite them back over. He politely asks Rosie if he can have her contact details.

'I've got plenty of spare time,' he tells her, 'it will be a change from the Times crossword.'

As they stroll back, Enid tells Rosie how impressed she is with Richard.

'What a charming man... and single. Not many men these days have manners like that. I'm just wondering though?'

'What about?' Rosie asks.

'Bessie Dora. What she might have got up to in that house?'

# Chapter 9

## *Making Plans*

Enid ties Monty to the bench and walks over to the grave. She kneels down and speaks aloud.

'Hello, Doug. I'm a bit later than I meant to be. Sorry. Rosie just turned up and wanted to show me something. I thought she might come with me but she wanted to stay in the garden and unwind. Not sure exactly what she is wound up about, but I know she misses you terribly.'

Enid leans closer to the grave and drops her voice to a whisper in order to confide in him.

'Here's a bombshell. Your mother worked at The Vine as a servant girl. What's more, she was Cornish, did you know that? From a little village called St. Tudy in the Camelford Valley. We've looked it up on the map and read about it. Apparently it's near Bodmin, although that makes me none the wiser. I've persuaded Rosie to take me there. Just for a couple of days. I'm remembering that you were sent to Cornwall when you joined up for the war. It was the talk of the village, you joining the navy and going off to Falmouth. That must have been the first time you left home. Seemed odd, being as Hereford was so far from the sea.'

She pauses, then makes an announcement as if she's very pleased with herself.

'I've asked Rosie if she will get me a computer. It'll be my new hobby, digging into the family history. I do hope I can unearth things that will make you smile. We always had such a laugh together, I would hate for that to stop. Oh, by the way, Monty disgraced himself yesterday. I told the neighbour he was your dog, not mine.'

'I hope your ears were burning,' she says to the dog as they walk back home.

Rosie sits down on the bench in her mother's garden, looking out over the hop fields. It was where she had often sat with her father. She closes her eyes and imagines he is still sitting alongside her. She doesn't speak aloud, but in her mind she calmly talks while he listens attentively.

*Hello Dad,*

*If it's alright with you, I'd like to have a little chat. I've been trying to understand why you always thought of yourself as lucky. I know you never measured luck in money or material things, just in terms of happiness and the good things that happened. I'm realising just how bad life started out for you. I hope there were some good years with your mum, Bessie Dora, before she ran away. Guess I shall never know the answer to that.*

*It must have been dreadful when she left. I know kids can be mean and spiteful and I wonder if you got teased about it. I'm told it caused a scandal in the village. Anyway, at some point things must have gone right for you. I guess you measured everything against the really bad times when it was just you and your dad.*

*I'm glad I didn't know about Bessie Dora till now, I wouldn't have been as forgiving as you. Had you told us the truth about what actually happened, her leaving you when you were so young, I think I would have hated her. I know you won't like to hear that.*

*Mum wants to take a trip to Cornwall. I'm not exactly sure what we are going to look for when we get there, but she's keen. We're going to start in St. Tudy where Bessie was born.*

*There's a family history centre in Redruth. Will says… I haven't told you about Will have I? I'll tell you a bit about him another day. Anyway, we're hoping they'll be able to help us in some way.*

*I hope you like me telling you all this. Mum seems to think we will find some good things about Bessie Dora. I can't see really what good it will do, but you never know, and it will be a break for Mum and me. Maybe there were other influences on Bessie's life, and it wasn't that she didn't love you and Arthur enough. Perhaps she felt she didn't belong in Herefordshire and wanted to go back to Cornwall. It can be a strong magnet, the place you come from.*

*I miss you, Dad. It's been good having this little chat, but I do miss you so.*

# Chapter 10

## *Trip to Cornwall*

They are driving down the motorway in Rosie's blue Golf with the satnav set for St. Tudy, Cornwall. Monty is sitting up on Enid's lap, staring straight ahead and barking if he spots a dog in another car. The journey is going well and they have not hit any hold ups as yet, but Rosie can't stop wondering about what they will do when they get there.

She is quietly wishing Will was here with her. She pushes the guilty thought aside. Just enjoy the time with Mum, she tells herself. They are booked into a small Bed and Breakfast, and there is a pub in the village which looks, from the website, to have a good menu. It seems very strange to Rosie that she is going on a sort of holiday with her mother after so many years. It could all be a wild goose chase, of course. Just because they have found out that Bessie Dora was born in St. Tudy doesn't mean they are going to get any further solving the mysteries about her.

'Mum, I hope you're not going to be disappointed. I really don't know what you expect to find,' says Rosie. 'I'm not sure this will bring us any closer to understanding Bessie Dora.'

'Don't worry. I'm just seeing this as an adventure, even if we don't find any answers.'

As they journey across Bodmin Moor the bleak, sweeping landform creates an impression of endless, empty space. They pass a signpost pointing the way to the old staging post of Jamaica Inn and Rosie secretly prays that they don't break down in such a remote spot. It all looks so unfriendly; not a tree in sight.

Enid is thinking what a contrast it is to the hop fields and hedgerows back in Herefordshire. The moor just seems to go on and on.

'It's not all going to be like this, is it?' she asks her daughter. 'It's so desolate.'

'I'm sure it's going to be very pretty once we get to St. Tudy,' Rosie assures her. 'The website claims that it's a picturesque village. Actually, I read that a famous person was born there and it's not our Bessie Dora. Would you believe that's where Captain Bligh came from, you know Mutiny on the Bounty and all that?'

Rosie sneaks a look across at her mother but Enid is sitting impassively, staring straight ahead. Her only action is to idly fondle Monty's ear.

'Do you remember the holiday we had in Cornwall years ago ? Your dad and I talked about going back but we never did. Then about a year ago he piped up and said that he wanted to move there, get a little cottage by the sea. I thought he was joking.'

'Do you think he knew, then? Did he know that his mother came from Cornwall?' Rosie asks.

'I don't know. I'm beginning to think he kept some things from me.' Enid ponders for a while and then continues.

'I'd love to know where Bessie Dora got the name Douglas from. It's always sounded so aristocratic for someone from such a humble background. It doesn't sound like a Cornish name, does it?'

'Maybe she named him after someone she had known, or somebody famous,' suggests Rosie.

'I thought that. I thought maybe she named him after Douglas Fairbanks, the film star. It could be she went to the cinema and had a thing about him. There was quite a scandal from what I've read. He had a fling with that actress, Mary Pickford, when they were both married to other people. Then they got divorces and married each other. All very romantic. You never know, that might have made a big impression on Bessie Dora.'

'Go on then, tell me a film that he starred in?' asks Rosie, as much to pass the time as anything.

'The Mark of Zorro, that was one of his films. Must be from the 1920's,' her mother replies.

They turn off the main road and follow narrow country lanes for about five miles. When they get to the village, they are struck by how tranquil it is. The rest of the world seems to be rushing on to Port Isaac or Padstow, while in St. Tudy nobody seems to be rushing anywhere. The church stands impassively amidst trees and bushes that are losing their leaves, and the old Clink next to the church looks as if there hasn't been a 'ne'er do well' to lock up since medieval times. Rosie thinks they have probably thrown away the key.

They ask a passer-by to direct them to the guest house as the village is a little maze of narrow lanes with no obvious street pattern.

The owner of the guest house, a well-dressed lady, makes a fuss of Monty, and they are given scones and dog biscuits as a welcome. She is happy to chat and tell them about the village and the church which she says dates from the fifteenth century.

Rosie has booked both the rooms in the cottage so that they don't have to share, and lets her mum choose.

'I'd like this one. I want to study this picture,' Enid says.

There is an old hand-coloured postcard of the village displayed in a frame on the wall. It shows the open space in the centre of the village by the blacksmith's shop, with the church in the background. The surrounding cottages are whitewashed with slate roofs and look charming and clean. There is no date, but the roads are of dirt and there is no traffic except for a horse and cart parked in front of the jail. Ordinary folk are going about their chores carrying milk in pails and a dog is drinking from a puddle.

They visit the church but find no gravestones with the name Tabb. Enid sits quietly on a pew inside, trying to decide how she feels. There is a strange unworldly feeling as if she is surrounded by people who know something she doesn't. There are secrets all around, she feels; she just doesn't know how to unlock them.

Rosie reads the potted history sheet about the church and the origins of the village. It tells of a St. Tudy of Landevennec, a Breton saint, from which the church gets its name. The graveyard is referred to as God's acre. Maybe that is why the place feels so peaceful.

They go to the pub and ask the staff if there are any families by the name of Tabb in the village, but no-one seems to know of any. The regulars at the bar are clearly pleased to have a new topic of conversation.

The landlord tells them that they get people coming here from all over, trying to track down their ancestors.

'A lot of it's to do with the nearby slate quarry,' he explains. 'Many slate miners left Cornwall and travelled to all corners of the world seeking work and then later, some came back again. It might be worth you going up the quarry,' he suggests, 'if your menfolk were miners. It's a right tourist attraction these days. I don't get it myself, it's just a whacking great hole in the ground, but people find it fascinating. We get people here for all sorts of reasons. Some of it's family history and a lot want to see where Doc Martin was filmed. We don't care as long as it keeps the pub busy.'

The following day turns out to be one of those incessantly drizzly ones. They opt to go to Redruth to the Records Office, although Enid is concerned they won't let her take Monty inside. The building seems fit for purpose, being antiquated. First impressions are that they have every record that exists in Cornwall, somewhere, but only the staff know where to find it. There are some outdated computer terminals for the public to use to look up census data and the like, but most records are catalogued in ring bound files under place names and districts, which are then cross-referenced to reels and reels of microfiche.

Enid asks about the dog.

'The dog is fine, my lovely, so long as it is well behaved,' the female assistant says, 'but you can't bring in any bags of food or drink, and on pain of death no pens or biros. Only pencils. Them's the rules. We've got lockers outside to put all your belongings in. Takes a pound coin, but you get it back at the end. Now, what would you like to look up today?'

Rosie explains that she knows her grandmother, Bessie Dora Tabb is from Cornwall, and is hoping to find out more about her and why she moved to Herefordshire.

'Alright, my lovely. I'll start you off here on our county records. Tabb is a good old Cornish name, we're bound to have some records.'

'I've got a Jonathan Tabb here on the records, born in 1867,' she says excitedly. 'Born in St. Tudy.'

She flashes something else up on the screen and her eyes scan back and forth.

'Now this census record tells us he was working as a farm servant at Polshea in 1881. So he would have been fourteen years old then. I can go and look up where Polshea is if you want me to. Just fill out this little chitty, there's no charge but you need to fill out a request form. Put my name in that box there, I'm Brenda, then I can go and hunt for things.'

Both Rosie and Enid agree that would be helpful, without really knowing why. They don't know where these places are, and are having trouble making any of this family history seem real.

There are several other people in the records office, apparently waiting for documents or information to be brought out from the inner sanctums. As they wait, they see a very old manuscript brought out with due reverence by another member of staff who looks very serious. He lays the enormous illustrated book on a special cushion on a far table. He demonstrates how to open the book without bending the spine. The privileged member of the public is issued with gloves. They watch as he turns the pages very carefully.

Rosie and Enid are feeling a little intimidated and out of their depth. They try to stop Monty from chewing the table leg. He starts to whimper, so they let him.

Brenda trots back over to them, clearly pleased with herself and cradling various maps and documents.

'I get such a thrill delving into the past. There's nothing better than having Cornish roots, something to be really proud of. Right, this is what I've found out. Polshea farm was owned by John Fortescue of Bosconnoe in them days and would have employed a lot of people. It's still a big dairy farm today, but of course it's all mechanised now. Here it is on the map, north of St. Tudy up towards Delabole. I've done you a photocopy to help you try and find it. Pretty countryside round there. Very pretty. How did you get on with the computer while I was away, did you find any other records for your family?'

'I'm afraid we got a bit distracted watching them bring out that great big leather bound book,' says Enid. 'It looks so old and fragile. We didn't think you would have records here going so far back.'

'Oh, we go way back. Let's try some other birth and marriage records, shall we?'

Again, the screen flashes and Rosie watches Brenda's head movements as she scans the data.

'Here we are, Bessie Dora Tabb, born 1895,' she says. 'Name like that, can't be more than one of those. So that must be her. There we go, we've found your grandmother!' she says looking across at them, delighted to have unlocked a piece of history.

'Jonathan Tabb was her father, then,' Brenda says, jabbing a finger at the computer screen. 'And there's her mother, Ellen Tabb.'

Rosie and Enid can't think of anything to say; it's all a blur.

'Alright, my lovelies,' Brenda continues, now in full flow. 'We should check on the census in 1891. Bessie won't have been born, of course, but we can see where Jonathan and Ellen are.'

Brenda knows the website inside out and is able to locate the record quickly.

'There we are, Jonathan Tabb. Yes, he's married to Ellen, and is head of the household, so they got married quite young. He's an agricultural labourer and carter, working at Delabole Barton for Mr. Greenwood. The barton bit just means lands or farm.'

'What I'd like to know,' asks Enid trying to keep up with everything, 'is where are the Tabb family living? We've been to the church at St. Tudy. It's a lovely little church, but we couldn't see any graves of any Tabbs anywhere. Would Jonathan and Ellen have got married there?'

'There's no quick way to find out where they got married,' says Brenda. 'You just have to go through the entries on the marriage register for St. Tudy. If it's not there, then we can look in the civil records.'

Brenda takes a roll of film from the drawer referenced St. Tudy and carefully slots it into the reading machine. She then goes off to help another member of the public, leaving Enid and Rosie to work the microfiche and painstakingly look at each entry of marriages for that church.

'What did she mean, civil records?' asks Enid.

'I guess she means a marriage in a registry office,' answers Rosie. By her mother's expression, Rosie can tell she doesn't like that idea.

After nearly an hour of trawling through microfiche, they decide they are getting nowhere, and Monty is desperate to find a lamp post or a tree. They tell Brenda that they are going to take the dog for a walk, and they are not sure whether they can focus on any more microfiche.

'Shall I have a look for you?' asks Brenda. 'You have a little walk and I'll take a gander. It's just that we had a lot of dissenters back then, especially up round Delabole way. They thought the church had deserted them. It's worth me giving it a try, my lovelies.'

'What did she mean by dissenters?' Enid whispers to Rosie as they walk out. 'I'm beginning to wonder what sort of family the Tabbs were?'

Ten minutes later, they have cleared their heads and Monty is physically relieved. When they go back in, Brenda is busy scribbling notes on bits of paper.

'I've found them!' she announces. 'They got married in 1889 at the Camelford Registry Office, that's up Delabole Way. I did tell you it got a bit wild up there. Your great grandmother,' she says, looking at Rosie, 'she was a Honey. I mean she was one of the Honey family and they've got history going way back. I know for sure there was a John Honey who was a slate miner, and I think one of the family became a lay preacher. Not sure he wasn't put in jail for a while. Anyway, this is the marriage entry for Ellen and Jonathan. Ellen's father is recorded as George Honey. I'll run you off a copy.'

Rosie and Enid are saturated with all the names and information.

They have reached the stage where they are not sure they can take anything else in, but Brenda's not done with them yet. Monty who has been patiently sitting by Enid's feet appears to yawn and then lets out a very loud fart.

'I've got records here of several children belonging to Jonathan and Ellen. Let me see, there are four children older than Bessie Dora, then after her there is a boy, Samuel, born in 1898 and Harry, two years later. Samuel and Harry were both baptised at their home by the Camelford Bible Christian Minister in 1901. No baptism record for Bessie Dora but that's not surprising. So there we are, Bible Christians, true dissenters. Does that surprise you?' Brenda asks.

We're getting used to surprises,' says Enid.

As they return the microfiche reels to the correct drawers, Brenda pulls out a faded document from the pile on her desk.

'I don't know whether to show you this, or not. It refers to a Jonathan Tabb, but the dates aren't right for your Jonathan, they are way too early, but it could very well be an ancestor. It's a bit torn and tattered but you can see it's an official document with the seal and everything. It goes way back to 1796, in the reign of George III. Do you want to see if you can read any of the writing?'

'What is it exactly?' asks Rosie.

'It's a bastardy bond,' Brenda says very matter of factly. 'Can you make out the names? It's a bit difficult as the lettering is very old fashioned, and the lower half of the document is water damaged.'

Rosie reads aloud what it says.

'*Elizabeth Reed, single woman, declared she is prignant with child and that the said child is likely to be born a bastard.*'

'I'm showing you this because Jonathan Tabb is the reputed father of the child,' Brenda says. 'Look, there's his name. If you read that, you can see that he has acknowledged the claim and put forward a bond of £50. He was married already, you see, and not in a position to marry the woman.'

'But that's not our Jonathan, is it?' says Enid defensively. 'It's not Bessie Dora's father. We don't know that this Jonathan Tabb is a relation, do we?'

'No, you won't know for sure until you trace your roots back,' Brenda explains. 'However, I'd have to say that there's a pretty good chance. Jonathan could well be a family name that they liked to pass down the line. They are not uncommon, these bonds. This one's from North Petherin. If you do trace your roots back and find that this Jonathan is related, then you'll know he did the decent thing in putting up the bond.'

They sit in the pub that evening with a glass of wine each, waiting for their meals to arrive. Both are trying to digest the information.

'It was just the relentless speed she kept throwing out names and dates,' says Enid. 'I was overwhelmed.'

'Yes, well she is used to dealing with all those records and documents, does it for a living. She really was very helpful.'

'Doesn't tell us how Bessie Dora ended up in Herefordshire though, does it? Did the whole family move, and why? I'm not sure how I'm going to tell Douglas about all this,' Enid mutters. 'It's all so confusing.'

'I'm trying to think what it must have been like so long ago,' Rosie muses. 'The little cottages we've seen, a lot of them are done up now, but back then they must have been very basic and bleak. And I'm trying to think of reasons people up and leave. It's usually to find work, isn't it? It's different now, of course. People move jobs and relocate just because of lifestyle changes. Back then they wouldn't have the luxury of choice. I mean it's still quite a poor area now, but back then, they would have taken whatever work they could. If that work dried up, they might have been forced to move elsewhere.'

She pauses and both are lost in their thoughts for a while.

'I don't really understand this religion angle,' her mother chips in. 'Brenda said they were dissenters. Were they being persecuted in some way, as in not being able to practise their own religion? I'm sure she said that one of them ended up in jail.'

At which point their food arrives.

Rosie has a restless night. She mulls over the information they were given, but feels that it has raised more questions than answers. In the morning, she suggests to her mother that they go back to the records office, and try again.

'Can't we just try phoning?' her mother suggests. 'I don't really want to make Monty sit through another session in there. I'd much rather see something of the countryside and look for some of those places she mentioned.'

Rosie makes the call and is relieved when it is Brenda that answers the phone. She tells her that they don't understand what is meant by the term 'dissenters'.

'It means they still believed in God, but they had lost faith in the Church of England,' Brenda explains patiently. 'A lot of people became Methodists or one of the other offshoots. There is a very good local history book for that area if you want to buy one. It explains it far better than I can. I do know that Methodists and Bible Christians didn't have licences for marriage till later on. So their congregation had to go to the registry office to get married.'

'But what exactly are Bible Christians?'

'They're sort of West Country Methodists,' Brenda says softly. 'They had elders meetings and some lady ministers, so in a way they were quite pioneering. They were strongest in the rural communities. There's a lovely Bible Christian church still in Tregony and if you go up to Delabole you'll see ever so many different churches. It was full of dissenting congregations splitting away as they had slightly different beliefs.'

'We're not very religious, just go to church for weddings and funerals,' says Rosie.

'I'm not religious either, and I have to be careful in this job about what I say so that I don't offend anyone. But that local history book I was telling you about, that touches on the subject as to why people fell out with the established church. It seems to me, it was really a question of which travelling Wesleyan or Methodist preacher caught people's attention, and whether they could abide by their codes and beliefs. Some wouldn't tolerate drinking, and as I said, others were more disposed to women having employment and allowing them to preach.'

'It all seems very unsettled and turbulent,' Rosie responds. 'I can see how my grandmother would have learnt to be independent and to question things. Question the church, question authority and conventions. Perhaps you learnt to look after yourself, and form your own beliefs.'

'My advice,' says Brenda, 'is go up to Delabole, breathe in the atmosphere, have a look at the quarry and some of the churches and take yourself back in time. A lot of the houses there haven't changed a bit. Be warned, though, if it's a drizzly day and grey, all that slate can look depressing. Try and think what it would have been like for Bessie Dora.'

# Chapter 11

### *Meeting up Again, Will and Rosie*

Will doesn't say anything about his daughter's wedding to start with and Rosie doesn't like to ask in case it didn't go too well.

'So, how was Cornwall?' he asks.

'Wonderful. Interesting. Frustrating. St. Tudy was a lovely little place. We sat for ages on the bench in the churchyard, just soaking up the feel of the place. When we saw the tiny village school, we thought Bessie Dora must have gone there. We seem to have thrown up more questions than answers though. We really needed to stay longer, but I'm thinking I'll go back again soon.'

'Maybe I can come with you next time. I know my way round Cornwall.'

She doesn't say anything to commit herself.

'Okay, I'll forget that one for the moment,' he says jokingly. 'Tell me what you saw and what you liked.'

'I happened to like Delabole, even if it was a bit grey and bleak with all that slate. We walked right the way round the open quarry. Monty loved it. Mum said she would have been scared being so close to such a huge hole in the ground if it hadn't been fenced off. You can't even begin to think how deep it is, and the water in the bottom was amazing. It was a kind of deep viridian, sometimes blue, sometimes green.'

Will smiles, and thinks to himself that he's never been asked to paint anything the colour of viridian. Maybe he ought to look it up on his paint chart.

'We were given a guided tour of the works,' Rosie continues. 'They've got old photographs of how it looked when the quarry was really booming. Hundreds of workers, not just men but small boys and girls, row after row of them, all lined up for a special photograph. Just think of the working conditions, though. The way the wind was whipping across from Bodmin Moor made us shiver. Some of the men did over fifty years service, can you imagine, in conditions like that? They must have been made of really tough stuff, to do that kind of work.'

Will nods.

'They showed us some of the slate tablets they used to record the days people worked. The workers' names were listed down the side and then there were columns and columns of little scratch marks. You know a bit like a school attendance register. I saw the name George Honey. The person who helped us at the records office told us that was Bessie Dora's grandfather. She suggested that when we've found out more, that I try and draw out a family tree.'

She pauses, but Will doesn't seem inclined to speak, although he appears to be listening attentively.

'How did the wedding go?' Rosie asks.

'You know weddings, drag on a bit don't they?'

'Your speech; you were alright with that, then?'

Rosie guessed he would have been terrified of standing up and addressing everybody. She had tried to suggest he keep it simple and sincere. She was as scared as he was about it going wrong.

'Actually, it was okay, better than I thought,' he says with a smile. 'I did what you said, just focused on one thing that was important between my daughter and me. We used to write letters to each other, you know after her mother and I split up. Now we just text of, course. But back then we took time. Time to write them; time to read them. I told her how wonderful that had been for me. I didn't want to embarrass her, but I said she was a great human being. I wasn't really talking to anybody else, just to her, to let her know we had a bond. Then I looked across and saw Selma, you know my ex… I thought she'd be smug, you know, waiting for me to cock it up like I always used to. Anyway, she had a nice look on her face. I don't mean I fancied her or anything, but she was smiling at me, gently, kindly. She didn't look like she wanted to kill me. So then I just raised a glass and said, '*To our daughter, Lauren, and to Selma. We got that so right, we couldn't have done any better.*' He paused.

'I was going to go on to say something else, you know, toast the bride and groom like I was meant to, but everybody started clapping and cheering so I just sat down and shut up.'

'Sounds good,' Rosie says, welling up a little inside.

'Better if you'd been there,' he answers, giving her a little hug.

# Chapter 12

## *Avenbury, the Abandoned Church*

Enid has been looking through her box of photographs again. She looks not just at the faces of the people but at the places where they were taken. She wants so much to visit those places again, especially the ones that were special to her and Douglas. She wants to take her daughter to those places and explain why they are special. Places like the abandoned church at Avenbury where she and Douglas used to meet. Enid has been re-reading more of his letters and they bring back such sweet memories of the times when they were courting and falling in love. She not only wants to see those places again, she wants to share them with Rosie, so that the memories can be brought alive and will be passed on.

Since the trip to Cornwall, she realises just how rooted she and Douglas were in their own small part of Herefordshire. The places where they both grew up and where they married and settled in a home of their own were all within a short drive of each other. She thinks of her husband and his feelings for the countryside. Working as a farm labourer brings with it a bond to the land, a tie to the area you were raised in, a feeling for your locality. It is something she shared with Douglas, an affinity with the place they grew up in, a love for the countryside, for the orchards and the hop fields, for the copses and the streams.

She has been thinking how different it must have been for Bessie Dora, to have grown up somewhere quite different and then to be uprooted, displaced. Bessie would not have felt an affinity for

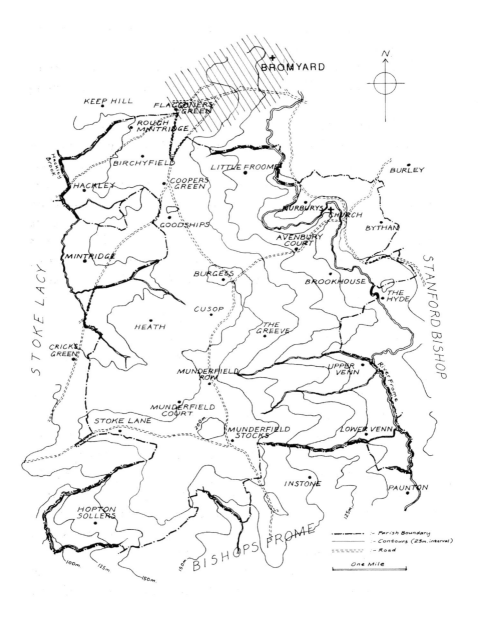

this local area, coming from so far away and from such a different environment. Did she resent leaving Cornwall? Did she have a choice in the matter? Enid wonders if she ever learned to love the area or did she always feel like a foreigner, like she was always in the wrong place.

Enid has not yet told her daughter that she sent off for a copy of the marriage certificate between Bessie Dora and Arthur. She found out how to go about it from the magazine, *What's in My Past*, the one Rosie had given her. Enid thought it might be interesting to see the names written down. Somehow, it might help to make Bessie Dora more real. The document turned up in the post yesterday and she has been studying it, and thinking about it ever since. She feels the need to share the certificate with Douglas, to read it to him while sitting by the grave. Monty has already been taken for a walk so she doesn't feel guilty leaving him behind.

She talks to her husband as if he was still sitting beside her.

'First thing that hit me was her signature. It's so like yours, the way she does the loop on the 'D'. Was she around long enough to help teach you to write?'

She has brought the marriage certificate with her, so that she can share the experience first-hand with her husband.

'I find it quite uncanny, seeing her actual signature. Anyway, this document tells me they got married at St. Mary's, Avenbury on the sixteenth of February 1920. Her age is given as twenty-four and she was a spinster. Now, my first question is how can she be twenty-four years old in 1920, when she told them she was twenty-one on the census in 1911? Something doesn't add up there. I think your mother might like to lie about her age,' Enid whispers.

'There's a space on the certificate where you fill in your place of residence at the time of marriage. They've both put down Callow

Marsh. That's the funny little cottage fronting the main road down by the Five Bridges Pub, which suggests to me they were living together before they got married. Isn't that shocking?' she asks playfully. 'It's such an odd little cottage and we've driven by it hundreds of times. Did you know that your parents lived there? You never said anything.' She pauses, as if she still expects Douglas to respond in some way.

'Your father, Arthur, he's described on the certificate as a fruit merchant. I think that's just a grand way of saying that he worked on a fruit farm and went round selling it. Do you think that's how he came to meet Bessie Dora in the first place? I mean the whole area around The Vine used to be nothing but apple orchards. He might well have been sent from one of the main farms to collect the fruit after harvest. Perhaps he took a shine to the servant girl when he stopped off at the house, or vice versa.' Enid pauses again.

'The other thing that strikes me from this certificate, and I've been reading up on these things, is that I don't think Bessie's parents were at the wedding and neither were Arthur's. The reason I'm thinking that is it's usual for the parents to act as witnesses. That's the custom, especially if the father has given the bride away. The names of the witnesses here are not the family names, they're not direct relatives. It's just two people by the name of Burbeck, whoever they may be. So it's my belief that it wasn't exactly a happy wedding to which everyone was invited. It's strange isn't it? Bessie didn't come to our wedding, and it looks like her parent's didn't attend hers, and neither did Arthur's. Suggests a falling out doesn't it?' Enid looks at her watch.

'I must get back, Doug. I've asked Rosie to drive me over to Avenbury. I haven't told her any of this yet. I want her to see the church first for a different reason, which you know all too well. The place where we used to meet. The place where you proposed to me. The place where, a few years later, I told you that I was expecting a baby… our little Rosie…' Her last words falter as the sentiment overcomes her a little.

'You can think of me later today, walking along those lanes just like I used to do all those years ago when I was coming to meet you after work. Bye for now, Doug. Love you.'

In the car, Enid chats away to Rosie telling her a little of the history of the church while at the same time giving directions on which road to follow. It's a maze of narrow country lanes but Enid knows every twist and turn. She has walked the road from Munderfield, where she grew up, to the church at Avenbury so often she could do it in her sleep. It was roughly halfway from where her family lived at Stone House to where Doug lived with his father on the outskirts of Bishops Frome, and would take her three parts of an hour or more to walk.

Enid never regretted having to walk so far. She enjoyed the time, thinking about what Douglas might have been doing all day and how pleased he would be to see her. She sometimes worried that he would be too tired to trudge over, having already walked to the farm where he worked at early dawn, and then the long hours of manual labour. He always showed up, however gruelling his day had been, a lovely grin on his face, looking as if he was the luckiest person alive.

Rosie is happy to indulge her mother on this little memory trip, but it seems as if the narrow lane is going on for ever, without any sign posts or passing places. She hopes desperately that they do not meet anything coming the other way.

Enid is momentarily lost in her thoughts. There is something else she finds uncanny. She thought she knew the place so well and yet she was never aware that this was the church where Bessie Dora and Arthur got married. It must have closed about a decade after their marriage. There was many a tale of a ghost haunting the church, which added to the spookiness of how it came to be abandoned in the first place.

Enid tells Rosie to park her car on the verge where the road widens for a short stretch. They walk up the lane and cross the bridge over the stream. It seems as if this is a forgotten part of Herefordshire. There is no noise from cars or tractors, no aircraft passing overhead and no people, except perhaps for silent ones from the past. The ruins of the church are hidden from view by ash trees that have self-seeded and which seem to sprout almost from the stone. Even when Rosie and her mother are within touching distance of the walls, little of the stone is visible as the ivy hangs dense and seems to choke the last life out of the building.

'Why was it abandoned?' Rosie asks.

'Not enough money to maintain it. There were too many churches in the area for the declining number of people. As you can see, there aren't many cottages round here and lots of people stopped going to church. The parish couldn't afford the upkeep of all the churches, and so closed this one. I think that was in the 1930s. I know my mother said she used to come here.'

Enid pauses for a moment and then continues more quietly.

'We used to meet just over there by the church wall, your father and me. In summer, I would bring a picnic and we would sit on the grass, or on the walls of the church. There was no roof, that was taken down a long time before, so if it rained, we just got wet.'

'It must have been a very romantic little church in its day, sitting in this bend of the river. Shame it looks so forlorn now,' says Rosie wistfully.

'My father was a churchman and he used to say it was a sign of a prestigious church if it stood in a big loop of the river like this one.

He was really surprised no-one stepped in to try and save it.'

'Were people buried here? What happened to them?' Rosie asks.

'They're still buried here as far as I know, but the stones were cleared away, I'm not sure where to. The land is no longer consecrated.'

They walk around to the rear of the church.

'There was always talk of there being ghosts in the church,' Enid says. 'People who came down here or passed by would say that they could hear the old organ playing or that they had seen the infamous Avenbury Knight. I didn't know whether I believed it or not. I didn't worry, I was here with your dad, but then one night he was late. I was sure that he would come. It was late autumn so it was a sort of twilight. The hops were hanging really heavy on the bines, just asking to be picked. They seemed to take on shapes as it got darker; they looked quite menacing and brooding. As I walked that last bit along the lane, I felt there was somebody behind the hedge, keeping pace with me as I walked along. I could hear breathing. I doubled back thinking that the person would stop or might even come out from behind the hedge. I began to get quite scared and I thought that if your dad didn't come soon, then I would go home. Except I really wanted to see him. It had got quite serious by that time and I thought that he might actually propose that evening.'

'It must have been very scary thinking there was someone there but not being able to see them,' Rosie says, thinking that if it had happened to her she would have run like the clappers. She was normally sceptical about ghosts and things but the way her mother was telling the story made the ruins of the church seem more dark and sinister.

'Yes, I was a little uneasy,' Enid recalls. 'As you can see, there are no houses nearby. No way of contacting anybody. I tried to be brave, but I was in quite a tizz when your dad finally showed up. I told him straight away that I thought there was somebody in the churchyard. Of course, your dad wasn't scared at all. Just hopped over the gate and into the field behind the hedge. After a few minutes, he called for me to follow him to show me what I had been scared of. It was a donkey. The lady up the lane kept a donkey, but I had never known it to be down by the church before. Your father thought it was most entertaining. 'That's what donkeys do,' he said. 'Follow you. Fancy you being scared of a donkey,' he kept saying.'

'Did he propose that night?'

'No, not that night. We only had an hour together. He hadn't even had his supper and he was still in his work clothes. He smelt of hops. Gave me a little hessian bag full of them, the best hops he could find, he said. Told me to put them in my pocket, then when I went to bed to put them under my pillow and dream of him. Told me I would sleep really well.'

'Did you?'

'No, I think I was really cross with myself for being scared of a donkey. I hoped he wouldn't tell my brothers and sisters.'

Whether or not she believed in ghosts, at this moment in time, Rosie rather liked the thought of still being able to communicate with a loved one after they were dead. Not exactly a conversation, but just little signs that connected you to that person. She loved the setting of the church, even if it was abandoned, knowing that it was a special place for her mother and father. The hedgerows and fields and cottages were probably not very different to when her mother and father did their courting here.

Rosie was glad her mother had brought her here. She was sharing that warm feeling of having a real sense of belonging. She could understand how it would be a comfort to her mother. Revisiting this place, breathing in the memories was surely a far better healing process than going on a cruise with people you had no connection with. She liked the solitude of the place. It was almost like time had stood still, and the rest of the world had passed on by.

'This church is where Bessie Dora and Arthur got married,' Enid says suddenly, breaking into Rosie's peaceful thoughts. 'I think that seems to add to the mystery of it all, really, the fact that this church was let go and abandoned. A bit like their marriage. Isn't that strange? A church that had stood for so long declining so soon after they got married here. I'll show you their marriage certificate when we get home.'

When Rosie doesn't respond, Enid touches her arm gently.

Her daughter hesitates.

'Mum, let's stop thinking about Bessie Dora. I'll look at the marriage certificate another day. I just want to think about dad for now. I am enjoying being here, thinking about him and you meeting up, having romantic encounters. Please, let's leave it at that for today.'

# Chapter 13

### *Will Follows a Hunch*

'You're quiet. Anything bothering you?' Will asks. They are talking on the phone, but Will finds Rosie isn't very forthcoming.

'Sorry,' she says. 'Bit preoccupied. I'm still trying to work out why Bessie Dora upped and left Cornwall. Did she run away? Perhaps she has a habit of doing that.'

'Like I said before, we need to go further back in time. We need to try and pinpoint when she left Cornwall. Why don't I do a bit of research on the websites? Thing is with ancestry, it doesn't always add up to start with, often because of names being written down wrong or people not telling the truth, for whatever reason. That's when you come up against brick walls, when their lies get recorded in black and white and it looks official. I got a bit of time tonight. Don't mind giving it a go.'

Later that evening Will types in the name Tabb. It might be a more common name in Cornwall, but round here it's not, so he widens the search to include similar names in case of any misspelling. He selects the date of 1901 and the computer brings up a census entry for a family by the name of Tubb. Will clicks on the name to bring up more information. Well, what do you know, he thinks. There are the christian names of Bessie's parents, Jonathan and Ellen. It's definitely them, but the mistaken entry explains why they didn't find it before.

He looks at the place name and district at the top of the form. Pendock. It's a tiny place on the border with Worcestershire. He looks at the names of the children. Henrietta, Charles, then Bessie Dora, Samuel and Harry. The records state that all five children were born in St. Tudy, Cornwall. The age recorded for Bessie Dora is six, for Samuel three, and for Harry, ten months.

Will writes everything down meticulously, recording where it appears on the website so that Rosie can look for herself. He checks the other entries that have come up in response to his search. There is the entry for Bessie Dora that they have seen before, the census for 1911 when she was working as a servant at The Vine. Will smiles to himself. He notices Bessie's age. Twenty-one. You were not, you little liar, you were most probably sixteen. He wonders why she would have lied. Mostly likely to persuade the employer that she had more experience of being a domestic servant than she really had.

He spends the rest of the evening on the computer, going further back in time to trace the lives of Jonathan and Ellen, finding out anything about them that he can. By the time he has finished it is past midnight. He feels it is too late to be phoning Rosie, so he texts instead.

*Can I pick you up early tmrow? We should go to Pendock.*

*Why? And where is it?* Rosie texts back straight away.

*It's a mystery. Show you tmrow xx* Will responds.


In the morning, Rosie is ready and waiting. She can tell instantly that Will is feeling pleased with himself.

'Bessie Dora. You've found out more about her?' asks Rosie.

'Yep. I found where she was in 1901, and that is why we are going to Pendock. The family must have moved from Cornwall that year or the year before. Jonathan, Ellen and five children.'

'How do you know?'

'Because it shows that all the children were born in St. Tudy, even

121

little Harry, and he was only ten months old, but on the day of the census in 1901, they were all living in Pendock, so they must have moved from Cornwall after Harry was born. I checked and that information ties up with everything else I found.'

'I can't begin to imagine how difficult that journey must have been,' Rosie says. 'I'm trying to picture how they would have got here.'

'With the horse and cart, must have been. I had another thought. Rather than trying to figure out what made them leave Cornwall, I thought about why they might have come to Pendock.'

'You mean they weren't so much running away as being attracted to something?' asks Rosie. So what was it? What would force a family with very young children to make a life changing move?'

'Couldn't figure it to start with,' Will says. 'I mean why Pendock? It's such an isolated, out of the way place. Pretty little church, but nothing much else except a farmhouse and collection of workers' cottages. Nothing really to come all the way from Cornwall for. But then I followed a hunch.'

He's enjoying the moment, teasing her gently about what he knows, but waiting before he lets go of the secret.

Rosie is enjoying the moment, too. She realises that through Bessie Dora they are finding out more about each other. Having Will help her search into the family history has made it better, more real. She's enjoying the experience, rather than being unnerved by it.

'The census doesn't tell us exactly which house they lived in,' Will explains 'but Pendock's only a tiny place so it'll be interesting. I thought we'd go to the churchyard first, it's usually a good place to start.'

Will leaves Rosie to look round the graveyard while he rolls a cigarette and stands by the gate, looking at the hills. After a few minutes, she comes back and shrugs her shoulders.

'I can't find anything. There are no graves with the name Tabb that I can see. Would they be buried here anyway if they were Bible Christians? What is it that I've missed? What have you found?'

'This grave here,' he says pointing, 'what do you notice about this one?'

'Well. It's bigger, more elaborate than the other ones, so it was probably somebody more important.' She reads the name: *Thomas 'Farmer' Greenwood.* Doesn't mean anything to me,' she says. 'Sorry, but I don't get it.'

'Read the inscription further down, at the bottom.'

'Born St. Tudy, Cornwall. Died Pendock. Will, That's amazing!' she cries out. 'I'm impressed. You knew this was here, how?' she asks.

He pauses.

'You're going to love me for this! I looked up all the people living in the district of Pendock on the census returns for 1901 to see if anybody else arrived from Cornwall at the same time as Bessie's family. In truth, there wasn't a huge number of entries to go through.'

'Not just a pretty face, are you?' she jokes.

'I found Thomas Greenwood and his wife and son, living in the big house next to the church and working a dairy farm with a hundred acres. Thomas and his wife and child were all born at Polshea, in the district of St. Tudy, Cornwall.'

'That can't be a coincidence, can it?' she asks.

'Nope. But you have to follow up these hunches in order to get the proof. So I traced Thomas Greenwood back to earlier times. He was the son of a big landowner down there, and there it was. Your Jonathan working for his father on a farm at Delabole Barton. So I figure Thomas would have known what a good worker Jonathan was, and trusted him. I also think Thomas wanted to make his own mark, not live in his father's shadow. He must have somehow found out that there was a dairy farm here for sale. Must have promised Jonathan a steady job and a better cottage, and that was it. If Jonathan was scraping an existence down in Cornwall and was struggling to look after his family, he might have jumped at the chance. He must have packed the cart up and they were on their way.'

'So what you're saying is that it must have been so desperate in Cornwall that Jonathan decided to take his chances with Thomas Greenwood? That must have been so traumatic for Ellen and the children, just to up and leave, not knowing what they were going to.'

'If you think about it, I reckon Jonathan must have been a strong character, got some real fight in him. They had two other children, older boys, Ernest and James. Looks like they found some sort of work down in Cornwall, so they might have stayed, or perhaps they moved up here later. I'm still trying to follow up on them.'

'I feel sorry for Bessie Dora. I think if I'd been told at six years old that the family was packing up and moving away, I'd feel lost and bewildered. She's being wrenched away to a strange place.'

'You've had a change of heart. You started off hating her,' says Will, laughing. 'Now you're feeling sorry for her.'

# Chapter 14

## *Richard Makes a Discovery*

Rosie feels guilty. She hopes her mother is not out in the garden as she drives by on her way back to The Vine. Monty is standing by the gate on sentry duty and he barks at the car, seeming to recognise her, but then he barks at most cars that go by.

Richard, the owner of The Vine, has emailed her, saying that he has some information relating to Bessie Dora. The wording was rather strange. *'It's rather delicate. Perhaps I can tell you, and you will know how best to tell your mother,'* was how he put it.

As Rosie pulls her car into the main driveway of The Vine, she thinks what a lovely residence it is and how immaculate the gardens are. It looks as if the gravel of the driveway has been freshly raked that morning and there is not a leaf or a twig littering the lawn. She admires the clipped box parterre and the rose garden with white marble statues. Richard cannot possibly do all this himself, she thinks. He must have a full time gardener. Her eyes follow the line of a cobbled path leading down towards a pond. She takes in the beauty of the flowerbeds and the backdrop of pleached hornbeam trees. She would love to have a tour of the gardens but thinks it would be too cheeky to ask.

Richard bounds out to greet her. His excitement seems to be heightened with a nervous energy and Rosie wonders if he is always this animated. He guides her through the house to his study which is at the rear, overlooking a more secluded part of the garden. He has laid out various books and diaries on his oak desk and has marked certain pages with leather bookmarks.

'These are the pages where there's a reference to Bessie Dora. We can take copies, if you like. I've got a printer over there.'

He pulls up a chair for her to sit down at the side of the desk. He exudes an urbane confidence. She notices his long slender fingers and well-manicured nails.

'I told you about John Zimmerman, the owner, didn't I?' He kept his own ledgers. Then there are a series of account books and house diaries filled in by his housekeeper, Jessie Tandy. Between the pair of them, I don't think they missed a thing. Every penny was accounted for and every bill recorded with details of payment. There are detailed records for all the staff, what time they had off for sickness or holiday, together with reports of any grievances or bad behaviour. As well as the house servants living in, there were other retained staff, including a groom, two gardeners and a handyman. So quite an establishment. It was only when I started looking into this for you that I realised just how meticulous the records are. Extraordinary, really. It was a very well run ship.'

He pushes two of the ledgers across to Rosie, and clears his throat.

'Perhaps I should leave you to look for yourself. I'll go and organise some tea. Earl Grey or Darjeeling?' he asks.

'Whatever you're having,' Rosie responds.

She opens the first ledger at the bookmark. It records the attendance of servants. She finds the name Bessie Dora Tabb and follows the column down to where there is an entry which says, *Transfer arranged to Laburnham House, Upton upon Severn, eleventh of November 1917.*

She turns the page of the ledger, and reads the entry: *Absent on account of being with child. Bessie Dora delivered of her child eleventh of December 1917.*

Rosie's first thought is to work out whether that child could have been her father. She gives a little shake of the head, and tells herself that her father was born in 1923, so no, that couldn't be him.

Richard returns with a tray of tea which he sets down on the corner of the desk.

'I've just got to the interesting bit,' Rosie says. 'What sort of place was it that she went to, this Laburnham House?'

'Not a poor house exactly, but it was an institution for unmarried mothers. It shows up on the accounts that her employer made a financial donation to have her admitted. She'd have been looked after there, and it got her away from this locality and prying eyes.'

'I presume she was dismissed, or asked to leave?' asks Rosie.

'Well, that's the curious thing. If you carry on through that ledger, you'll find that she was back here a month later. Now normally, as I understand it, servants that had bastard children would have been sent packing. Excuse me for using that expression. But not her. She came back to The Vine and carried on working right up until after the end of the war. Possibly the child stayed at Laburnham House for a while as there is a record of a further amount being paid, but I'm not sure.'

As Rosie sips her tea, she gazes across at Richard. He has his head still lowered over the ledgers as if by staring at them for longer will unravel some of the anomalies. He seems genuinely concerned at what has happened to Bessie Dora. More than that, he seems afraid that what he has found might be upsetting to her and her mother.

'It's all very odd. I've spent quite a time puzzling over it,' he says. 'It doesn't seem to follow the familiar sad little tale of a servant girl having an illegitimate child and being booted out. It's far more complex than that.'

Rosie takes another sip of her tea. She sits there wondering what could have become of the child.

'There's something else you should know,' says Richard. 'John Zimmerman's son Ulric, he upped and went away from here at exactly the same time. Of course, it could just be a coincidence. I think they were much the same age, Bessie and him. My mind just began to wonder about the circumstances... and why Mr Zimmerman would have paid for her to have the child. I did wonder—'

'Do we have any evidence that there may have been something between Bessie and Ulric?' Rosie butts in.

'No, not really. Of course, it was common knowledge that the father, John Zimmerman, was very close to his housekeeper after his wife died. He couldn't marry her, but he left her a substantial legacy in his will. Maybe his son thought that if it was acceptable for his father to hob-nob with the servants, then it was alright for him too.'

Rosie smiles at the term 'hob-nob'. It sounds so pompous and old fashioned.

'Where did Ulric go?' she asks.

'He somehow got involved in the war. He didn't have to, as far as I can see; he wasn't called up. He was a bright boy, quite a scholar. Gained a research scholarship at Birmingham University. The diaries record him being in France briefly and later Salonica, as a dispatch rider. He loved motorbikes, apparently. Would have been dangerous for him, of course, being a Jew... lots of prejudice. John Zimmerman wasn't happy about him going. Thought he would take over the family business.'

'Did something happen to him?'

'He was killed in the war. I don't know any details.'

They finish their tea and make polite conversation for a while.

Rosie drives back towards her mum's house, and wonders what exactly she's going to say. Her mind is in a tangle. She thinks back to the ledgers and diaries that Richard had shown her. The facts couldn't be doubted, but how did you unravel the circumstances? How could you find out what had actually gone on? Clearly, Bessie Dora had a child before getting married to Arthur, but who was the father?

Rather than turn into the driveway of her mother's house, she decides at the last minute to drive on by. It's not that she doesn't want to see her mum, it's just that she hasn't worked out what to say. Without really thinking, she drives down to the church where her father is buried and parks in the lane. She doesn't feel like going to the grave, so she just sits and thinks about her father. She hopes it will help clear her head.

She fumbles in her handbag to find her mobile and calls Will.

'Will. I've found out some things.'

She tells him quickly how she and her mother had walked over to The Vine. How they had happened to meet the owner, Richard, who was taken with the story of Bessie Dora and wanted to help them by looking into the records that existed at the time she worked there.

'Richard emailed me yesterday,' she says. 'I went back as clearly he had some news, and he said it was delicate and he didn't want to tell me while Mum was there.'

'So, he asked you to go back on your own? Didn't you find that a bit odd? And how was he able to contact you as you don't give your details out normally?' Will asks tetchily.

'This was different. It was about Bessie Dora, and he was only trying to help. He's a nice man. He showed us around the servants' quarters up in the attic. It was really touching to think that Bessie Dora slept there.'

Rosie realises that Will is just a little jealous.

'Will, listen. The records at the Vine show that Bessie Dora got pregnant and was sent away to have the baby. It seems that Mr Zimmerman, the owner at the time, arranged for her to go to a sort of charitable house. You have to think that she was sent away to try and keep it all hushed up, don't you? It seems he made a financial donation to have her admitted. The housekeeper recorded that she gave birth to a child on the eleventh of December 1917; that was years before she married Arthur.'

'So I don't see why you needed to go round on your own, unless this Richard character was trying to chat you up. Why is he so interested anyway?'

'I thought you'd be pleased that there was some news. What seems really odd is that Bessie went back to work at The Vine for Mr Zimmerman a short while afterwards. We're not sure what happened to the child, whether it was adopted or whatever, but Richard has a theory that the son, Ulric, might actually be the father. That's why John Zimmerman took an interest and made sure Bessie was looked after.'

'I still don't see why you needed to go round there on your own,' Will spits out.

'No I don't know why, either. I actually think it's because Richard is a bit of a prude. I don't know why he felt he couldn't tell Mum about Bessie Dora getting pregnant, but some old fashioned men are like that. But it's an interesting theory, isn't it, that Ulric might have been the father? Richard is going to carry on digging to see what else he can find out.'

'I don't suppose he's got any evidence to back this theory up?' Will snaps.

'Only really that if the father was hob-nobbing with the housekeeper, as he put it, then the son and the servant girl might have decided that it wasn't such a crime after all. Richard says that

John Zimmerman left the housekeeper a considerable legacy in his will. That just fuelled the rumour that she was more than his housekeeper.'

'Richard may have a point there,' Will says a little grudgingly. 'I remember thinking it a bit odd when I read the census return that Zimmerman filled in himself. He wrote down *Lady Housekeeper*. There was a separate column for gender so he didn't need to say that. He could have just put housekeeper or servant, like most employers would, but he gave her a title. That was endearing, but all it shows is that the father was fond of the housekeeper; it doesn't shed any light on what the son got up to.'

'We don't know when or how she met Arthur, but Richard says...'

Will groans. 'I'm getting a bit fed up now. Are you seeing this Richard again, then? I thought it was you and me searching for Bessie Dora.'

'No. It's not like that. Will, don't spoil this for us.'

'Sorry,' he says. 'What we need to do is send off for the birth certificate of the child. See what that brings up. You've got a definite date and place of birth, so it shouldn't be that difficult.'

'And the certificate will give us who the father is. Now isn't that going to be interesting? Rosie chuckles.

# Chapter 15

## *The Girl in the Photograph*

Enid listens attentively to what her daughter has to say.

'I sent off for the birth certificate a few days ago. It arrived this morning. The baby was a girl. Bessie named her Monica and registered her with the surname Tabb. I was expecting it to tell me who the father was, but the space for the father's name is just a blank. It's so frustrating.'

'I knew something went on in that house, I could feel it,' Enid says. 'She's got a secret or two, Bessie Dora, hasn't she? Not sure what Douglas is going to say. How do I tell him that his mother was a bit of a *strumpet?*' she says the word quietly, under her breath.

As Rosie pours their coffee out, Enid thinks to herself about the dates. She goes to get the photograph which is sitting on the dining room table, the one of Douglas as a little boy with an older girl by his side.

'The daughter that Bessie had in 1917 can't be the girl in this photograph with your father. She'd be older,' says Enid. 'The girl here, the one Doug told me was Sarah, she's only a couple of years older than your father, three at most. So there has to be another sister that Doug didn't know about. Bessie must have had another child. What on earth happened to her?'

'We're not really sure what happened,' Rosie responds. 'Richard and I wondered if she might have been adopted.'

'We don't know when Bessie met up with Arthur, do we? Enid asks. 'Of course, the war was still going on in 1917. Arthur served in the war, I remember Doug telling me. He wasn't a great hero or anything, but he did his bit, and got injured in the foot. From what your dad said, he was sent home not long before the war ended.'

'The thing about the birth certificate though,' Rosie explains to her mother, 'is that it doesn't necessarily mean that there was doubt over who the father was, just that he wasn't around at the time of the birth. I googled it so that I could understand the legal side. An unmarried mother registering a birth back then couldn't put the father's name down if he hadn't agreed to it or wasn't actually present. If Arthur was the father but was still away fighting in the war when Bessie gave birth, then the Registrar would not have allowed her to put his name down.'

'Well, of course Arthur is the father,' says Enid. 'Who else would she meet? They must have just jumped the gun a bit. Then if he was away, in France or wherever, he might not even have known the girl was born. I'm not sure many letters got through in those days.'

'Richard has another theory. Of course he hasn't got any proof, just certain things seem a little strange. Mr Zimmerman's son, Ulric, he was the same sort of age as Bessie. Maybe a few years older as she clearly lied about her age in order to get the job as servant in the first place. By my reckoning, she was twenty-two when she gave birth to Monica. Richard wonders if there might have been a 'dalliance' as he puts it, between Bessie and Ulric.'

'But she married Arthur, didn't she, just a few years later, and had two more children. Why would we think this other man had anything to do with it?' Enid asks her daughter.

'Because he was sent away just at the time that Bessie Dora had the child. He then got caught up in the war, served as a dispatch rider in Salonica. Of course, we don't know exactly what happened, but the records at The Vine show that Mr Zimmerman paid to have the child looked after. We know they were very wealthy people, they owned a silversmith's business in Birmingham, but would they have paid to look after the child just out of charity or was there another reason? Monica; it's not that common a name, is it? Where did that name come from?' Rosie asks.

'I expect Bessie just liked the name,' says Enid. 'We never knew where she got the name Douglas from, did we?'

'That's true. All I can say is that Richard is very persuasive about it all. When I was there at The Vine, he sort of convinced me that Ulric was the father.'

'It's so frustrating, trying to work out what happened,' says Enid. 'It's like a jigsaw with half the pieces missing. What's more, we haven't found out anything good about Bessie Dora, have we? I don't think I'll say anything to your father just yet. I'll stick to telling him about the garden and what Monty has been getting up to.'

'What has Monty been getting up to?' asks Rosie.

'Oh nothing too awful. I'm trying to see it from Bessie's point of view,' Enid continues. 'There were a lot of unmarried mothers during the war, it wasn't that uncommon.'

'I don't think Bessie would have gone back to her own folks when she was in trouble. Being religious, would they have taken her back?' Rosie muses. 'She might not have been in a position to be too picky, with such a shortage of men after the war. If Arthur was willing to take her on, she might have settled for him just to get a roof over her head. Perhaps she never really loved him.'

'It was certainly a turbulent marriage by all accounts,' Enid replies.

'I don't know what to think,' says Rosie. 'Will, the friend I was telling you about, he says there's no firm evidence at all that Ulric had anything to do with Bessie Dora, and he doesn't like the idea of the rich and privileged taking advantage of young servant girls.

Of course, the circumstances could be entirely different. Bessie Dora may have been a gold digger for all we know. So Will is rather fighting Arthur's corner. I'd like you to meet him, if that's alright?' Rosie asks, trying to make it sound casual.

'Certainly, dear. Do you want to ask him over for Sunday lunch or would that be too formal?'

'That's fine, I'll ask him. He's got some ideas as to how we could follow up on a few things. We need to try and find out what happened to the girl, Monica.'

'If she's anything like Bessie, goodness only knows,' Enid tuts.

# Chapter 16

## *Disappearing Act*

'You're not nervous are you, about meeting Mum?' Rosie asks after she tells him about the invitation to Sunday lunch.

'No. Should I be?' Will answers. 'I won't be cross examined or vetted, will I?'

Rosie laughs. It's always good talking and being with Will. He's uncomplicated. She feels at ease with him and with herself.

'No, of course not, but it might be a little strange for Mum and me. Sunday lunch was always such an occasion when Dad was alive,' she explains. 'He loved it, looked forward to it all week. Roast dinner, lots of vegetables, nearly all grown in his garden. Pudding, a crumble, or something else homemade. I'm not sure what Mum's been doing of late. Can't think she's been going to all that trouble.' She pauses, then says, 'I'm not worried about her liking you, of course she will, but she's ... well obviously she's a little withdrawn at the moment. I just don't want it to be awkward in any way.'

'Shall I bring some veggies from my allotment. Would she like that?'

'I didn't know you'd got an allotment. You never said.'

'Well, I didn't think it was the most exciting thing about me. I mean, if I was internet dating, I wouldn't put it down as a main interest, would I?'

'Have you tried that then... internet dating?' she asks coyly.

'Only the once.'

'And?'

'It didn't go well.'

Rosie decides to let the matter drop. He can tell her sometime if he wants to, but she thinks it's not really relevant, anyway.

'Will, where else can I look for Bessie Dora? If we could only find some things out before we go over there on Sunday, it would be great. She just seems to have done a disappearing act after leaving Arthur. People can't just disappear like that, can they? Where else did you look when you were looking for your father?'

'In a way, I got lucky. I knew his profession, signwriter, and I was told at some point that he had a strong accent, from the Black Country, you know from around Dudley. So I asked where I could look up trade people from that area, and I was told Kelly's Directories. There he was. It leapt out at me. It all fitted.'

'So where can I look? Rosie asks. 'All that was ever said about Bessie Dora was that she became a nurse, but we've no idea where? If we could only get to see the later census records, that would tell us where she went to after she left Arthur. When are they going to be made available for us to see?'

'You'll have a long wait. Didn't you know, the 1931 census records were destroyed during an air raid on London? We can try looking at the 1939 register, that's really important and pretty accurate.'

'What's that?' asks Rosie.

'It was a complete stock take of the nation. If you think about it, we were getting ready for another war. The government needed to know what resources they'd got. How many people, what ages, who could fight. They also had to have information so they could issue identity cards for food rationing and all sorts of things. It's difficult to believe now but people had to carry their cards way after the war ended.'

They sit together at the computer. Rosie has put a slow casserole to cook in the oven, and they have a bottle of wine to open if they feel like it. The two of them have withdrawn into their own little world. She wonders at his patience looking for any records that might fit with Arthur and Bessie Dora.

Arthur proves easy enough to find on the Register. They look at the information together, digesting what it means. 'Resident at Bishops Frome, Herefordshire. Single, and with a child living at home.'

'I think that child must be your dad,' Will tells her.

Rosie is shaken by the poignancy of that word, 'child'. A few months later he'd left home and changed from being a child to volunteering to serve in the Second World War. Douglas would have grown into a man almost overnight.

Will gives Rosie's hand a gentle squeeze to signal he understands how she must be feeling.

'Arthur being described as single is relevant. It means he must have been divorced by then.'

'I wonder how old Dad was exactly when she left? 'Rosie asks, her voice quavering just a little.

'I might just try going back on the ancestry records to see when Arthur was divorced.'

After a while, he finds the entry and reads aloud, 'He petitioned for divorce in 1933. Look it's here on the 'Find my past' website. Arthur, asking for a decree nisi from his wife, Bessie Dora, address unknown, on the grounds of misconduct. The notice appeared in the Gloucester Citizen newspaper. So I guess the divorce must have been granted on that basis.'

He thinks for a minute. 'I don't think it's too relevant that it appeared in a Gloucester paper,' Will continues. 'I'm guessing nobody thought she lived there, and I don't think that Arthur expected her to respond. It's just one of these legal hurdles you have to go through.

It's the West Country equivalent of posting a notice in the London Times. At least it gives us a date for when Arthur had stopped trying to save the marriage, if he ever did, that is.'

'Poor Arthur. I guess he realised by that time that she wasn't coming back. Dad would have been just ten years old,' Rosie says tearfully. After a moment, she looks up at Will and realises that this might be opening up some painful memories for him too.

'Did you ever find out why your parents had you adopted?'

'They weren't married and I think she was an alcoholic. They tried to make a go of it for a while but, well, you know.'

He goes back to staring at the computer.

'I don't understand this. I'm bringing up all the records for 1939, and the computer says it's found Bessie Dora but when it brings up the page, all the names are blacked out, like they've been censored for some reason. I don't know why. I can't think. Here look. It brings up somewhere called the Monyhull Colony, King's Heath, Birmingham. But then when you scroll down the list of people there, all the names are obscured, every single one. I don't know whether it was something to do with the war, or other reasons for keeping the names a secret.'

Will seems about to say something else, but then changes his mind.

'What? What is it?' asks Rosie.

'This colony. It was an asylum, a sort of mental hospital.'

Rosie looks at the computer screen. 'A hospital for the epileptic and feeble minded,' she reads. 'Oh no, what have we unearthed?' she asks fearfully.

# Chapter 17

## *The Scrapbook*

Enid has settled herself on the bench within eyesight of Doug's grave. She wants to have a good long chat with him, and thinks the grass is a little wet for sitting on.

'First thing to tell you, Doug, is that Rosie's got herself a chap. His name is Will, doesn't like to be called William, and I like him. Didn't know what to make of him to start with. Thought he looked a bit scruffy with his torn jeans and T-shirt, but he seems very thoughtful and considerate. He's been taking a real interest in Bessie Dora, and researching a lot of things. He looked up Arthur's war records. It seems he was away in action for much of 1917, but he did come back home for a short while. We spent quite a time discussing whether he could be Monica's father or not. We worked out that she must have been conceived in March. Turns out the records show Arthur going back into action in early February. So unless the birth was a little overdue, Monica may not have been his. Of course, none of this is really conclusive, but we are wondering why it took them so long to get married if Arthur was the father.'

Enid thinks to herself that she really wishes she had got to know Arthur better when he was alive. There are so many questions now that she wishes she had asked him. Not directly about Bessie Dora, obviously, that would have been impolite, but about how he coped with everything.

'We know Arthur was injured and sent back to England to convalesce, but that was almost a year after Monica was born, and just before the war ended. Unfortunately, the records don't tell us exactly where he was sent to, they just list it as a private house. It could be The Vine because Rosie has found out they took wounded soldiers in there. The alternative theory is that he only met Bessie Dora after she had the baby, and it wasn't his after all.'

She tugs on the lead as another family with a dog come into the graveyard and Monty, thinking he has the one and only claim to the space, barks aggressively.

'I got the feeling that Will and Rosie had stumbled across something else, something they didn't want to tell me. There were a lot of glances and nods going on between them. Will started to say something about Birmingham, but didn't go any further with that. Apparently your mother did a very good disappearing act, though.'

She pauses again. The family with the dog are looking at her. Enid realises she must look a little mad sitting there having a good long conversation with herself. Never mind, she thinks she has earned the right to be just a little eccentric these days. She wonders what she will do with the rest of her afternoon and evening. She is feeling just a little lonely.

At work, Rosie is sitting beside her boss in a management meeting. She sneaks another look at her watch, but it's still telling the same time as the last time she checked. The meeting is all to do with the impending office move to centralise the housing association. At present, the different sections are spread about the town in old, outdated buildings. A brand new building will accommodate them all, with an imposing glass atrium at the entrance. The section heads around the table are arguing about how much space they require and which floor they should be located on.

Only the Director and Rosie know that the meeting is futile, since the office layout has already been decided. In fact, the very first day the preliminary plan was received from the architect, her boss took a felt pen and drew lines of demarcation for who would go where. The meeting taking place now is just a PR exercise, a so-called opportunity for the section leaders to feel they can make an input and will be listened to. It was a sham.

Rosie has that nagging feeling that there are far better things she can be doing. She hasn't been concentrating too well at work and reports and forms are piling up. This business of Bessie Dora and the mental hospital wasn't helping. Did it mean there was a strain of madness in the family, or had Bessie simply gone off the rails? Did that explain why she walked out on her family? Had she had some sort of breakdown?

Deep in her daydream, Rosie is suddenly aware of someone's mobile phone going off. That is so rude, she thinks. Didn't she issue a staff instruction just the other day that all phones had to be switched off in meetings, with no exceptions. It was a really loud ring tone as well. She becomes acutely aware of the others staring at her, some looking cross and others faintly amused.

With a never to be forgotten walk of shame, Rosie grabs her bag and escapes the room.

'Mum, what's wrong? You never call me at work. Are you alright?'

'I'm fine, dear, but I've got Richard here. He says he's got some exciting news and he wants to see you right away. I'll put him on.'

'Mum, no—'

'Hello. It's Richard. Richard Price from The Vine. We've had the most extraordinary piece of luck. You need to see what I've found.'

'Richard, I'm at work.'

'I'm happy to come to you, go for lunch or something. Or perhaps you'd rather come to The Vine later. It's just so astonishing, I wanted to show you straight away.'

Rosie thinks of Will, and how he's not going to be happy with that arrangement.

'Richard, can we meet at Mum's house? I'm sure she'd like to be involved first hand in anything exciting. I'll leave early, get there about six, hopefully.'

She heads back towards the meeting room, wondering what excuse she can make to explain her mobile ringing.

'Rosie, I've had the most wonderful afternoon,' Enid says, bubbling with enthusiasm as she opens the door to her daughter. 'This charming man has been here all the time, and we've talked and talked. Lots of things make sense now. I'll go and put the kettle on and then we can get started properly.'

There are newspaper articles strewn all over the dining table.

'Where did they all come from?' Rosie asks.

'From a scrapbook kept by the housekeeper at The Vine. She was the one that was very close to John Zimmerman, he left her quite a bit of money in his will,' Richard explains.

'Yes, I remember. Her name was Jessie.'

'Jessie Tandy. She's written little notes to go with some of the articles and there's the odd letter or two. It's all very touching. She was devoted to John and to the son. I see that although he was actually christened Ulric, the family always seemed to call him Ulrie. I guess it was the name they called him as a child and it stuck.'

'He was killed in the war, wasn't he?' Rosie asks.

'Yes, but it was an accident. There's a piece here about it here,' Richard says, clearly upset by the event. 'Can you believe it? An accident in wartime. He just took a bend too fast, lost control of the bike.'

143

Richard passes her a press cutting. She begins to read:

*Ulric Zimmerman was tragically killed when he lost control of his Douglas motorcycle while serving in the Royal Engineers Signal Service. He was 28 years old and had served for just five months when the accident occurred.*

Rosie looks down the article to see if she can find the date when he died. September 1917 it says.

Richard guesses that she is trying to work back the dates in her head, to see if they tie in with when Monica was born.

'It fits in with when we know he left The Vine,' Richard starts to explain.

'So if Monica was his daughter, he would never have seen her. That's very sad,' Rosie says wistfully.

'From this scrap book, I don't think there can be any doubt that Ulric was the father,' he says. 'It's just so fascinating that Jessie kept all these articles and that they've survived. The scrapbook was on the shelf with all the other ledgers and records. I didn't bother to look at it to start with. For some reason, I thought it was going to be full of recipes and Women's Institute articles and the like. Then when I moved it, that newspaper cutting fell out, so I went through the whole book. What a good job I did.'

Enid comes back in with a mug of tea for Rosie and a glass of sherry for herself and Richard. She makes the excuse that they've drunk enough tea to 'float a clipper' as she puts it.

'I'll take you through everything we've found,' Richard says. 'Enid can let me know if I miss anything out,' he says gallantly. 'It's all related to the Zimmermans really and their house in Birmingham. That was where their main house was, in Kings Heath, and of course their business was in the jewellery quarter. It seems that baby Monica was taken to the house and was brought up by John

Zimmerman's younger sister. Monica was a sweet little thing apparently, and everybody loved her. Being as Jessie had a somewhat close relationship with John Zimmerman, she got to hear most of what went on there, and she also got regular letters from her fellow housekeeper.'

'We think Bessie must have agreed to this arrangement,' chips in Enid. 'She probably didn't have any alternative really, seeing as the child was being well looked after.'

'Yes, Bessie stayed on at The Vine,' Richard continues. 'She did some training as a nurse after the baby was born. It was during the latter part of the war and The Vine was being used as a convalescent home. John Zimmerman was heartbroken when his son died. Whether he felt guilty in some way we shall never know, but that may be partly the reason he let the house be used in that way. Bessie may have been inspired to go into nursing by seeing the wounded soldiers. It certainly must have seemed a desperate time with so many men dying. Including Ulric, of course.'

'Is there any clue as to why she took up with Arthur?' Rosie asks. 'Was she encouraged to do that?'

'We couldn't find anything about Arthur,' answers her mother. 'Most of the cuttings and things are to do with Monica. There's even a school report from when she was about eleven.' She finds it amongst the pile of things on the table and passes it over to her daughter. It reads:

*Monica is well spoken, extremely kind hearted and quick to learn. She is not particularly gifted at languages, but has a good aptitude for sums, algebra and business matters in general. She is also showing good skills at cookery and sewing.*

'That sounds a very superior school. Do you think they kept Bessie informed of what was happening to her daughter?' asks Rosie.

'I'd like to think so,' answers Richard.

'Something has just dawned on me,' Rosie announces. 'When we started, I thought you were going to tell me something awful. You see, I thought Bessie Dora was sent to a mental hospital, because she had a breakdown or something. That's what I found out the other evening, that she went to somewhere called the Monyhull Colony. Guess where that is? Kings Heath, Birmingham. So it can't be very far away from where the Zimmerman house is. But now I understand. She wasn't an inmate, she was a nurse. I'm guessing that Bessie Dora went off there to be near Monica. So she chose to work at a mental hospital, an asylum as it would have called in those days. That must have taken some strength and spirit. Bessie Dora must have had a heart of gold to work in a place like that.'

# Chapter 18

## *A Bombshell*

Rosie is looking forward to the gig at the Majors. Will is going to pick her up so that they can go together. She thinks back to when she went along to hear him play for the first time and laughs at herself. Back then she snuck in and didn't want to talk to anyone. How things move on. Now she's happy to get there early to bag a table at the front, and maybe even try some of the food. She'll stay right to the end, talk to other people, and be happy to hang around till all the gear is packed away. It's a work day tomorrow, but it won't matter if she doesn't get in at the stroke of eight. She's got so much flexitime stored up, she might as well use a little.

She's thinking she should plan a trip out for her mother. Perhaps they could go to Birmingham, to Kings Heath, to see if they could see this Monyhull place for themselves. It's converted now of course, into luxury flats. She looked it up. So it wouldn't be a bit like the old days, when it was an asylum. It must have been a foreboding place for anyone that worked there, let alone for the poor inmates, she thinks. People with mental disorders wouldn't have had a choice in those days, they were just sectioned and put away.

She had watched the latest *Who Do You Think You Are?* programme last night. That involved taking more than a few skeletons out of the cupboard, but then the researchers found the ancestor had some redeeming features, so the episode ended on a high note and the celebrity went away happy.

That's more or less how it's been with Bessie Dora, she thinks. A few ups and downs. Her grandmother certainly had a few amoral tendencies, but clearly she wasn't all bad.

It would be good to go to Monyhull, Rosie decides, and she hopes that Will can come with them. There must be some records somewhere about how it was in the past. As Will has said before, it just involves a little detective work in finding where the information is kept, and finding the right person to help them unlock the secrets.

Rosie laughs. She knows her mother likes to go and tell Douglas all the latest revelations. Now, at last, she'll have something really positive to say. Yes, Bessie Dora may have left her children, but there does seem to be a reason. Maybe she thought the people in the hospital were in greater need.

Rosie hears Will's car pull up outside. After a quick look in the hallway mirror to check her hair is reasonably well behaved, she slams the door behind her and goes to greet him.

'Are you ill?' she asks him, having opened the car door and looked inside. 'You look awful.'

He motions her to get in.

'I've got something to tell you and you're not going to like it.'

'Will? What is it? Is it something about us? Is it about Richard? I explained that. He's just being helpful, and I didn't see him alone, he came to Mum's house. I've already told you I'm not attracted to him.'

'It's not about Richard.'

After a moment or two he continues.

'Look. Let's get to the pub, get a drink. Find a quiet table. Then I can show you something.'

'You've got me really worried now!' she says anxiously.

They get themselves settled inside. The pub is already buzzing, and Will is relieved that the other members of the band have shown up on time for a change and are busy getting the equipment set up.

Andy has got the drum kit sorted and is trying to untangle the leads and wires.

'It's about this,' says Will, handing her an official looking brown envelope marked General Register Office.

'What is it?'

'It's a marriage certificate. Well, a certified copy of a marriage certificate,' he explains dryly.

'Are you trying to tell me that you're still married?' she asks.

'It's not me. It's Bessie Dora. She got married again, to a Belgian soldier, and she lied about her age, big time.'

# Chapter 19

## *Leon*

Rosie wakes the next morning and goes downstairs to make herself a cup of tea. She stops for a moment before turning on the kitchen light, hoping that it might all have been a bad dream. She flicks the light switch and there it is on the kitchen table. A single sheet of green and white paper from the General Register Office.

They had stayed up discussing it until about two in the morning, but nothing seemed to be any clearer. Rosie remembered nothing of the music the band played at the Majors. She had a vague recollection of a lot of cheering at the end, and then Will putting his arm round her to guide her outside.

There was no mistaking it was Bessie Dora. Her full name was there on the official paper, even giving her maiden name of Tabb. It stated she was the divorced wife of Arthur John, and it gave her father's name too, Jonathan Tabb, retired carter. Her profession was listed as mental nurse and her residence, The Monyhull Colony, Kings Heath.

Rosie knows this is her grandmother, but who is the man? Leon Bruneel, Corporal 0676 in the Belgian Army. Rosie had difficulty reading his home address. It looked like Rue Menuisies, somewhere in Brussels. He was listed as thirty-one years old, the divorced husband of Cheresse Bruneel.

Will had tried to explain that there was no reason why two divorced people shouldn't get re-married. It wasn't illegal or anything. The marriage had taken place at the Register Office, Birmingham, on the

1943. Marriage solemnized at ....The..Register..Office.............................................in the
District of .....Birmingham...............................in the ..County..Borough..of..Birmingham...............................in the

| When Married | Name and Surname | Age | Condition | Rank or Profession | Residence at the Time of Marriage | Father's Name and Surname |
|---|---|---|---|---|---|---|
| 1 | 2 | 3 | 4 | 5 | 6 | 7 |
| Twelfth August 1943 | Léon Bruneel | 31 | Divorced husband of Chacese Bruneel | Corporal 0676 Belgian Army | hospitalised former home 10 Rue Mauricies woluwi St. Lambert Brussels | Francois Bruneel (deceased) |
| | Bessie Dora Booton formerly Tabb | 38 | Divorced wife of Arthur John Booton | Mental Nurse | Monyhull Colony Kings Heath | Jonathan Tabb (retired carter) |

Married in the ..Register..Office....... according to the Rites and Ceremonies of the ............... by licence before by me

This Marriage was solemnized between us

L.Bruneel
B.D.Booton

in the Presence of us,

V.S. Lambill
C.Groin

C.E. Priest
Registrar

151

twelfth of August 1943. A lot of hasty marriages took place then, Will told her, with the war still raging.

It was the lie about her age that most shocked Rosie. It said on the document she was thirty-eight years old. By anybody's reckoning that was a lie. She would have been nearer forty-eight or thereabouts.

After a while, Will tried to make a joke about it.

'Somewhere on the way to the Register Office, she lost ten years,' he said, laughing. 'She could have said anything, it's not like they check. I wonder if Leon ever found out?'

Rosie was not finding it the least bit funny. She thought she had finally got to know her grandmother and had found out something good about her. Rosie felt proud Bessie had trained as a nurse, and had almost certainly met Arthur that way. It was a story she could empathise with. Having a child when she was a servant girl, now just seemed innocent. Events had rather overtaken Bessie, that was all, and that happened in such turbulent times as war. It was harder to excuse her leaving Arthur and walking out on her other children, but even that bitter pill was softened by her working in a mental hospital.

Now Rosie was back to not knowing what to think. Her grandmother seemed to be someone who deceived people and constantly lied about her age. What a little madam. Rosie wasn't at all sure what her father would have thought of this. She checked her diary for work. She hadn't got anything important to do that day, so she emailed her secretary to say she was having the day off. A little qualm of conscience made her add that if anything urgent cropped up to give her a call. She would go over to her mother's to break the news, and leave it to her to explain things to Douglas.

As it happened, Enid was a great deal calmer than Rosie about the revelation.

'How would she have got away with it? That's seventeen years older than him!' was Enid's initial comment. 'I don't know whether to admire the sheer brazenness of it, or feel mortified that she's married a soldier under false pretences.'

'It doesn't look as if any of their families were present,' Rosie comments. 'The names of the witnesses don't correspond to anyone we know. Perhaps they dragged them in off the street or maybe they worked at the hospital. You would have expected Bessie's daughters to have been there, wouldn't you? We know that Monica would have been in Birmingham. I wonder what on earth she thought of her mother?'

'We mustn't judge her, Rosie. We don't know the facts. She's working as a mental nurse. God knows what that must have been like in wartime.' Enid thinks for a few minutes, then continues.

'He must have been a patient, mustn't he? Wounded in the war or shell shocked or something? Maybe he was dying and she married him out of compassion. Maybe he was blinded and he fell in love with her voice and thought she was a sweet young nurse. If she didn't want to disappoint him, she might just have told a little white lie when she had to give her age.'

'That's an uplifting story, but I'm not sure we're ever going to prove any of it,' Rosie answers.

They wander out into Enid's garden and watch as Monty chases a rabbit out of the flower bed. Enid makes a fuss of the dog, but Rosie can't help thinking how upset her father would be over the damage to the plants.

'Will and I are going up to Birmingham on Saturday, just to take a look at Monyhull. There's a park nearby, so if you want to come, we can take Monty with us. Not sure whether we can find out anything, but you never know.'

'I think we should go,' says Enid. 'We've got to try and solve the mystery of Bessie Dora for your father's sake.'

# Chapter 20

### *The Monyhull Colony*

Enid didn't know what she was expecting exactly, but with a name like The Monyhull Colony, she thought it was going to be something foreboding. The description, which they had read before, *for the epileptic and feeble minded,* was chilling.

'It's not called that any more, Mum. It's had all sorts of names over the years, hospital, asylum, but they're all long gone.'

They drive along Monyhull Road, a tree-lined avenue, up to the original house. It's a white-painted, imposing Georgian building with expensive cars parked outside. Rosie parks her Golf in a visitor's bay, and they take Monty for a walk on his lead. The building, now called Monyhull Grange and converted into apartments, looks grand amid new planting and landscaping. It is hard to view the smart luxury flats and think what it must have been like as a walled asylum keeping the incarcerated away from the rest of society.

They walk round to look at the building from all sides, but it doesn't want to give away any of its secrets about the past. The history of the place seems to have been removed. It's as if the building has been cleansed, sanitised, with nothing left on the site to act as a reminder of what it was like in the last century.

They walk past a modern children's play area and a jogging track, both of which are deserted. Whatever went on here, whoever was helped or shut away, their ghosts seem to have gone. Nearly everything from the past has been torn down.

'I read that much of the land was sold off for housing,' Will says.

'That brought in money for restoring Monyhull Grange and the church. All the other hospital buildings were demolished.'

Rosie begins to feel the place has nothing to tell them, and that their journey has been wasted. New houses have been built all around. They walk over to the church, which sits a little aloof. Inside there is a plaque, dedicated to three members of staff who died while on duty during an air raid in 1940. Enid and Rosie stare at the inscription. They think for a moment, think back in time.

'Bessie Dora would have been here then,' says Enid. 'How terrifying that must have been. All those epileptic patients… they must have been traumatised. I'm realising how very brave she must have been to work here.'

They write their names in the visitor's book with a note to say how beautifully kept the church is. Enid adds a comment about the place feeling very tranquil, and how nice to have fresh flowers on the altar. Then on impulse, she writes, *God Bless you Bessie Dora, for your work here.*

They put some money in the donations box. After a few more minutes, they feel they have exhausted everything there is to do. They walk back towards the door, with Monty tugging at the lead.

A man appears behind them as if from nowhere. He looks at what they have written in the visitor's book, and barks out a stage cough which echoes round the church.

Rosie turns and looks at the small man who has wire-framed spectacles. She feels sure he is about to tell them off for bringing Monty inside. She picks up the dog, much to Monty's disgruntlement.

'The name you've put in the book. I recognise it,' he says. 'Did you have family here, when it was a hospital?'

'Yes. Yes, we did. My grandmother. How did you know?' Rosie answers, looking hard at the man.

'Is that why you've come? To find out some history? I can help you with that, if you'd like. My name is Nigel. How do you do?'

He shakes their hands and pats the dog.

'My father was the Registrar at the hospital, responsible for all the admissions and everything else that needed to be recorded. Unfortunately, he had a very idiosyncratic way of organising things and his writing was appalling. The Monyhull Trust was going to junk the lot, but I offered to catalogue everything and put it on a data base. I trained as an archivist, so I like to think I've done a good job.'

They follow Nigel into a small vestry. He finds some extra chairs from behind a curtain and invites them to sit with him at the computer. Nigel apologises that it will take a few minutes for the computer to open up.

'It's not exactly the latest technology,' he explains.

'Why was it called a Colony?' Rosie asks.

'It goes back to Victorian times and earlier, of course, when we used to lock people away on a huge scale. A lot of the Victorian do-gooders were concerned with genetics. To put it crudely, it was thought best to stop what they called mentally deficient people from breeding, so there was strict segregation of the sexes. I'm pleased to say the patrons here had altruistic motives; they wanted to help people that were more a danger to themselves than to others. We treated people who were termed sane epileptics and feebleminded. Excuse the terminology, but it was a different era. It was very much a closed community, mainly because of the fear and shame felt by people on the outside.'

While Nigel talks, he clicks away at the computer.

'During the wars there was an influx of wounded soldiers, so it became very overcrowded. In 1940, my father recorded over thirteen hundred people living at Monyhull.'

'Gosh,' is all that Enid can think to say.

'Now,' he says, turning to look at Rosie, 'let's look for your grandmother.'

They look through the records. They find Bessie Dora.

'Yes, she was one of the long serving mental nurses; came to work here in 1931. Her daughter, Sarah, was a nurse here later on.'

'We think Bessie came here to be near her other daughter, Monica,' adds Rosie. 'We know that Monica was living nearby.'

'I've got that name, too,' says Nigel, clicking on the mouse and looking intently at the computer. 'She joined us here much later when the war started. She was aged twenty-two then. Worked as a nurse and then in 1942 she went overseas to do service for the Red Cross.'

'So she would have been away when Bessie married Leon,' Enid declares.

Rosie explains to Nigel that her grandmother married a soldier when she was here. A corporal in the Belgium army.

'Leon Bruneel was his name,' Enid tells him.

'Ah, yes, we've got a copy of the marriage details on our records. Leon was a patient here.'

'Do we know what happened after they got married? Where they lived?' Enid asks Nigel directly as she can't follow the records on the computer screen.

'They got married on the twelfth August 1943,' Nigel says, his eyes still on the screen. 'He died on the twentieth.'

'That's heartbreaking. Poor Bessie,' utters Rosie.

'It's what I thought though, isn't it?' Enid says quietly. 'She married him out of compassion.'

Nigel explains kindly that they have little further information. As a married couple they would have been entitled to have private accommodation, and a copy of the marriage certificate was placed on record for that purpose. Leon was not well enough to be moved, Nigel told them, so he stayed on the hospital ward.

After a few minutes, Will breaks the silence with another question.

'What we couldn't understand is why all the names of people working here were blanked out in the 1939 register?' he asks.

'The censorship thing. Yes, that was all very strange. For some reason, patients and staff in mental hospitals were all obscured on government records. You've got to realise that the culture and propaganda at the time was to keep information secret and not to trust anyone. There were a lot of rumours about chemical warfare and the like. Some said that it was being developed and tested in the hospitals. It seems fantastic now, but in those days the rule was to *keep mum*. I think it was innocent enough. They were just paranoid about not letting intelligence fall into enemy hands.'

Nigel has been looking up other records while he has been talking.

'I see from our records that your grandmother's maiden name was Tabb. That's flashing up on the system, too. I must have cross referenced it with someone. I'll just take a look.'

He calls up the records and finds the name Samuel Tabb.

'Samuel was a patient here from the First World War. He was admitted in 1916, aged eighteen. Brown hair, five feet five inches tall. Just a little lad, really. Could he have been a relation of Bessie's do you know?'

'There was a Samuel,' says Will. 'I remember his name, when we found the first census records for Bessie. That would have been her younger brother. How did he end up here?'

Nigel looks down the record sheet on the screen, and passes on the information.

'Either he didn't tell them about his early epilepsy, or they thought he was lying to get out of active service. Anyway, he was sent to the front. Had a fit almost immediately. There were convoys of wounded soldiers arriving here regularly at that time. A whole section of the hospital was set aside for shell shocked cases and discharged epileptic soldiers. Of course all those buildings have been demolished now. They were pretty shoddy.'

'It must have been awful here,' says Rosie.

'It wasn't as dreadful as it sounds, mainly because of the dedication of the people working here. My father used to speak of it being like a family.'

'I'm afraid to ask whether Samuel recovered?' Enid says.

Nigel looks back at the screen.

'Samuel lived here until 1931, working on the farm, looking after the cattle and the pigs. That's what most of them did, work on the farm or in the laundry. It helped to rehabilitate them and of course, it was free labour. It says that he had a cheerful disposition and liked working outside. The case notes say his death wasn't expected but that he had a minor seizure, after which he was confused. He then had another more serious seizure and died. I'm very sorry.'

'Hang on a minute,' says Will. 'You said Bessie Dora started working here in 1931. Did she come here to look after Samuel, then?'

Nigel peers at the computer screen.

'Bessie was officially employed as a nurse at the Colony from the first of February of 1931. The records show that Samuel died on the twenty-first of January of the same year. So the answer to your question is no, she didn't nurse him.'

'But she came here at almost the same time. There has to be a reason for that doesn't there?'

They wait while Nigel scans the records in front of him.

'What I can tell you from the records here is that my father and the guardians of the Colony met Bessie Dora to discuss where Samuel was to be buried. It says here that the ashes were released to her. She said it would be Samuel's wish to be taken back to Cornwall, to where he was born as that was his real home.'

# Chapter 21

## *Back to Herefordshire*

Nobody speaks for a while when they get back in the car. They are all trying to make sense of what they have been told.

Rosie breaks the silence. 'Is it too much of a coincidence that Samuel should have gone to Monyhull, with Monica being so close?'

'I don't think so,' Will answers. 'It was such a huge mental hospital, and one specialising in epilepsy and taking discharged soldiers. It would be the obvious place for Samuel to be taken when he was discharged as unfit.'

'Did she leave Arthur and her children to go and look after Samuel? Is that what drove her to leave?' Rosie asks.

'Nigel said she wasn't employed there as a nurse until after Samuel had died,' Will replies.

'Well, something inspired her to go and work there as a mental nurse,' Rosie says, 'and I don't think it was just to be near Monica. Maybe she knew Samuel was ill and went there to help.'

'I'm guessing it was the final straw,' Enid tells them. 'When I think back to what my parents told me about her and Arthur, it was a stormy marriage by all accounts. She stuck with it though, long enough to have Sarah and Douglas. She tried to make a go of it. So something must have snapped with her. If she got word that Samuel was in trouble, she might have felt she had to go to him.'

'Yes, I can see that. If word got to her that Samuel was ill,' says Rosie 'and she must have known that he was epileptic, so she would have feared the worst. I bet she was desperate to go and see him. Then if Arthur was unsympathetic, uncaring, perhaps she just decided to go anyway.'

'We don't know that she intended to leave for good,' Enid says. She might just have wanted to visit Samuel and see Monica. Then when Samuel died, perhaps she decided to stay and help others like Samuel. As you say, something must have snapped in her.'

'It doesn't explain everything though, does it? We know it was only Douglas that was living with Arthur when the petition was made for the divorce, so Sarah had moved out by then. Bessie Dora must have sent for Sarah to join her in Birmingham. Why didn't she want Douglas with her as well?'

After a few more miles they cross the county border into Herefordshire, and Enid feels she is beginning to understand. Thoughts begin to fall into place in her mind.

'I think I can answer that now,' she says. 'I think it was in her nature to try and look after people. I think she knew that Douglas would be happier with Arthur, and that Arthur would care for him. Douglas would have hated to leave the countryside. I know that for a fact.' She thinks a bit more and then continues.

'Although she walked away from him, I believe she did care something for Arthur, and couldn't take Douglas from him. She wouldn't have wanted Arthur to be on his own,' Enid says. 'Douglas always carried on loving her. He never had any ill feelings towards her, never once spoke badly of her.'

'Maybe it's significant that Arthur never remarried,' Rosie says. 'Most men would have with a young boy to bring up. Dad would only have been about seven or eight, wouldn't he, when she left? It must have been very hard for Arthur.'

'All I wanted when we started this was to be able to tell Douglas that his mother was a good person,' Enid says, 'that she had a good heart. To work in a mental hospital for all those years, with bombs dropping, she must have been dedicated. I couldn't have done that.'

Enid asks Rosie if they can drop her off at the church on the way back as she wants to have a chat with Douglas. She doesn't think it fair to keep the news from him. She kisses her daughter goodbye, saying that she will walk back home when she has finished at the grave. It will be good for her and Monty, she says. After a moment's hesitation, and a slight touch of embarrassment, she gives Will a hug.

Rosie drives Will back to her house and she makes them both a coffee.

'You've been so brilliant, Will,' she says, 'helping me with everything. I wouldn't have been able to unearth half the things that you did. What do you think of Bessie Dora now?'

'I think she was an exceptional lady. She married a soldier from both the first and the second world wars. I don't think many women have that claim to fame. I think you should be proud of the good things that she has done.'

'What do you think we should do next?'

'I think we should go down to Cornwall and have a look. We may not find anything else, but it seems like the right thing to do. I had a hunch before, remember, and that worked out okay.'

'The thing is, Mum and I looked all over the graveyard in St. Tudy. There wasn't anyone by the name of Tabb buried there. So, if Bessie took Samuel's ashes back there, perhaps she just scattered them somewhere. We certainly couldn't find a marked grave.'

'Looking for a grave isn't the only reason I want to take you to Cornwall,' he says with a smile.

# Chapter 22

## By the Graveside

Enid takes a moment or two to compose herself. Monty seems to be behaving well enough so she sits down on the ground and lets him off the lead. He doesn't seem inclined to wander off and she turns her attention to telling Douglas what they have found.

*Hello Doug.*

*I wish you could have been there this morning, at Monyhull, to see where your mother worked, although there wasn't really anything of the hospital left.*

*She did quite a disappearing act, Bessie Dora. Little wonder nobody knew where she'd gone to. It was a separate world, walled off from the rest of society. She was a nurse there, looking after soldiers and other people who were epileptic.*

*Your mother was a really good person, full of compassion and dedication to her job. Her younger brother had epilepsy. She must have known that when they were children in Cornwall. He was at this place, this hospital, and he died there. She would have been so upset about that. So we think she left you and Arthur to help him and others like him.*

*Your sister, Sarah, she became a nurse like you thought, and Monica, she worked for the Red Cross. They were all so dedicated in what they did. Bessie would have influenced them. I'm so proud of you that you never felt angry towards her. You always felt she had goodness in her and you were right. Those instincts of yours.*

*I wrote a little message in the church at Monyhull, where she worked,* saying *God Bless her for the work that she did. I know we've never been very religious but it seemed like the right thing to do.*

*What's most important to me is that Bessie Dora passed on such good qualities to you, and in turn to Rosie. Kindness and generosity. So I am grateful to Bessie for what she did and who she was.*

*I would have liked to have got to know Bessie Dora and I've never thought that before. I know now that she gave up an awful lot, too. She wasn't around to see us get married, or to see Rosie growing up, but she went to somewhere she felt needed. She made a difference to other people. She made a life for herself, and it was a life worth living.*

*Rosie has been so good helping me with this. I could never have done it without her. I do hope she isn't troubled by anything that we have found out. Hopefully she will have Will there to care for her. He's nice. You'd like him, and they seem good for each other. I'm hoping they make a go of it. Not that I'll interfere, of course.*

*It's been an adventure trying to solve the mystery of Bessie Dora, but we can rest easy now. We don't need to look any further.*

*Good night, my love. Sleep well.*

# Chapter 23

*Back in St. Tudy, Cornwall.*

'I get a buzz from being here,' Rosie says. 'I never thought I'd want to live anywhere other than Herefordshire, but this place, I really feel something for it. I did when I came with Mum.'

They head for the bench at the rear of the churchyard, which faces out towards the village school. Rosie stops to admire a carved angel on top of an old gravestone. Despite its age, the carving is well preserved and beautifully crafted. She runs her fingers over the figure and as she does so, she has a curious feeling of wellbeing, of comfort, of making sense of a jumble of feelings. The name on the grave is Rebecca Kellow. It does not mean anything to her, does not ring any bells, but she thinks it a lovely name. She finds herself wanting to know more about Rebecca. Someday, when she's not so busy she'll look into her history.

Will caresses her fingers with his own, as if to bring her attention back to the present.

'We've been all round this graveyard,' she says with a sigh. 'There's no stone here with the name Tabb. I told you. Mum and I looked before.'

They head for the gate at the far end, the one that is overshadowed by the yew trees. Rosie's eye is caught by the movement of a mistle thrush looking for berries. There's a patch where the brambles have grown up and they notice a few simple memorial stones set into the wall. Will stoops down under the yews and finds a stone urn so deep in colour that it was lost in the shadows. He feels the solidness of the stone, the smoothness of it. He pulls aside the branches of the tree and the light picks out the veins of the polished stone so that the swirls and the original colours stand out.

'That is amazing,' says Will. 'That is real serpentine stone.' He traces his fingers over the carved letters in the stone, and turns to look at Rosie. 'I think you might want to come closer and see this,' he says gently.

Rosie reads the inscription aloud.

*Samuel Tabb 1898 – 1931.*

*Beloved younger brother of Bessie Dora.*

'I wish I could have known her. It seems so wrong, really, not to have known your own grandmother,' she says. 'It's been so difficult trying to piece it all together and with Bessie not here to speak up for herself.' She thinks for a moment.

'Sorry,' she says. 'That was insensitive. You didn't even get to know your parents properly, let alone grandparents.'

'No,' says Will, 'but I found what I was looking for, and that was to know a bit about them. It helped to make sense of where I'd come from. I managed to find my dad, and a bit about my mum. It helped me to understand why I find things difficult at times.' He is quiet for a moment.

'You've had something of a bumpy ride with Bessie Dora, haven't you?' he says. 'Firstly hating her, then distrusting her and later feeling sorry for her. Remember you did all this because of your dad, to see if you could find out something good about Bessie. He hoped that she found something in her life, that it wasn't always sad for her, and I don't think it was. She had a hell of a lot of difficult stuff to deal with. She lived through two world wars for a start. And being uprooted from here as a child. I wonder she thought anything in life was safe or secure. And then Samuel dying. I think she found solace in a place that was set apart from everywhere, behind walls. It wasn't right to leave your dad, but then you think of all those people she helped and cared for.'

'Perhaps I can understand myself a bit better now, says Rosie. 'Why I shy away from certain things. Why I get withdrawn at times, and feel I can't cope.'

They leave the churchyard in silence. As they pass through the gate, Will takes her hand. She finds his touch warm and reassuring. They linger by the old blacksmith's shop as they walk back to her car.

'It was a lovely feeling, 'reflects Rosie. 'It was like Samuel was hiding in the shadows and we brought him out and recalled his memory and that of Bessie Dora. It was so uplifting. It means they are not forgotten.'

'Do you want to look for anything else?' he asks. 'We could delve further back in time. You must have ancestors here, before Bessie Dora.'

'You know, Will, I feel very contented with what we've found here. I'm not going to be haunted by any demons, or worried that I might have inherited certain genes or family traits. I can see that Bessie Dora was full of love and kindness. I'm sure my father could sense that and so he just accepted what happened, without any bitterness or hatred towards her.' She stops for a moment and turns to look at him.

'I don't feel the need to look back any further at Bessie's past. Not for the moment at least,' she says, smiling.

'Think I'm always going to have a warm feeling towards her for bringing us together,' he says softly. 'Maybe we should raise a glass tonight and drink to her past and our future?'

'Right now, I've got my mind full of the present,' Rosie says, leaning towards him, 'and I'm very happy with that.'


# *End*